Moving From Idea to Finished Draft

by Cat Rambo

Table of Contents

Moving from Idea to Finished Draft

Cover design and book formatting by Jennifer Williamson.

Acknowledgments

To my students, who teach me as much as I teach them.

Introduction

This class grew out of a question that kept getting posed to me by students. Over the course of several years, I spent a lot of time thinking about the best answer and it finally occurred to me the answer was actually a different question.

Their question was this: *How do I tell a good idea for a story from a bad idea for a story?* They were asking that because they knew that sometimes they started with ideas that never got completed. We all have that folder with at least a few half-finished stories in it—some that only got as far as a few lines; others that border on being done, but sharing this trait: something stopped us from completing it to the point where it was ready to go out the door.

Stories all come from different places and processes will differ from person to person, situation to situation, and even story to story. But I have found that becoming a better writer is not about knowing how to distinguish the good ideas from the bad, but rather trusting myself to be able to take any idea—even one that is incomplete, flawed, or cliché—and do something worthwhile with it. The question you should be asking is: *How do I learn to take any idea and turn it into a story?*

That is the answer that I try to provide in this book. After working your way through it, you should be able to take a story idea and do the following:

- Identify what sort of starting point (or combination of starting points) you have.
- Choose among several possible strategies for fleshing it out.
- Know what needs to be supplied to make it a complete story.
- Move it from idea to finished draft.

Galloping through the book may not be the best approach. In fact, I'm pretty sure it's not. Even working your way through it front to back on a schedule may not be the best choice.

What I suggest is that you take it in smaller chunks, doled out a bit at a time. Give yourself time to think about the material as well as to notice manifestations of it in what you're currently reading. Keep a notebook of passages and sentences that you think work particularly well, so you can try to figure out how they're achieving the effect that they are, and keep dissecting them as you learn more about the internal factors of a story.

You will get the most out of the book if you do some of the exercises, but you may find them particularly effective if you do so in conjunction with a current project, using aspects of that work as a base for the exercises. If something works well for you, you may want to incorporate it into your writing practice.

I have included "overachiever versions" for those who want to take the various writing exercises farther. I tend in that obnoxious and somewhat competitive direction myself, and so if you really want to sharpen a particular skill, I've included ways to do each exercise at greater length or with a higher difficulty setting.

Translating the book from online course into book form has been an interesting challenge, particularly since I have undertaken a move with typical writerly egotism and used my own work to illustrate the concepts. This is actually due to laziness; I have rights to my own work and thus did not have to track down copyright stuff. Shazam!

Now let us begin.

SECTION 1
Ways Into Stories: Structures

Chapter 1

PLOT

What it is

Some stories start out in your head as a plot. This is a complete story: you know the problem, some basics of the characters, and what will happen. Perhaps it's something you've generated or taken from elsewhere. Perhaps it arrives pre-made in your head (and you should glory in it when it does, in my opinion), so all you need to do is sit down at the keyboard and write it out.

If you can describe in a few sentences what will happen in a story, you know the plot. For example:

- A little girl takes cookies to her grandmother and encounters a wolf along the way. When she gets to her grandmother's house, the wolf is waiting to attack. A nearby woodsman comes and kills the wolf. (Little Red Riding Hood)
- A man steals the defense plan for a planet that is immensely

wealthy. When he tries to use it, he finds out that the defense is constructed out of (left unspecified because this is a spoiler of an excellent story, and you should go read it) and meets a terrible fate. "Mother Hitton's Littul Kittons", by Cordwainer Smith)

What it provides

You know the overall flow of the action: this happens so this happens so this happens and then it ends this way. You know the basic story pattern: tension increases until the climax, and then rapidly falls. You know the source of the tension and usually the basic conflict: how the wants of two or more entities are colliding in some fashion.

You have some sense of where the story begins and a stronger sense of where it ends (although the reverse is not impossible). Connie Willis says to begin at the moment when the problem becomes a crisis. I don't know that I agree that you should always do that, but it's certainly better, in terms of story tension, to start with a moment where the problem is already taking place than to start with the placid moment before anything starts to happen.

You may or may not know the characters involved, but you have some broad basics, and know some of the things about the character that affect it most for you, which will probably include gender and approximate age.

Similarly you have some broad basics of the setting, the overall world of the story, although you may need to think of specifics pertaining to scene locations.

More importantly, often you have an impalpable feel for the story, a sense of the overall tone and emotion that will shape the words as you write. To make the most of that, spend a couple of moments thinking about the atmosphere of the story. What might you compare it to in terms of movies, works of art, pieces of music, poems, or other creative forms? What is the overall emotion, both yours in writing it and what you want readers to take away?

Considerations

What do you bring to the story that makes it unique? There are only so many plots (opinions of the actual number differ, with some saying seven, others numbers like three or even thirty-six), and the fact of the matter is that at a certain level you will not be able to do anything genuinely new unless you are more of a genius than I.

So figure out what you do definitely bring to the table: the unique details of your life and experiences, your emotions and understandings, and your sensibilities. What instances of this plot have you witnessed being played out in your own life—perhaps as actor, perhaps as audience—and what of that experience can you draw upon?

Specifics of the action may be lacking in your broad overview, in which case you will need to flesh them out. Your burglar steals something - what? Who owns it and what defenses against thieves do they have? Your bounty hunter is chasing her prey, but what crime has that prey committed? Specifics of the location are something that you may well need to develop in detail, in which case think of the most engaging aspects and use those as interesting backgrounds to color a scene. Make that important conversation take place while the two are racing on ice skates through a city's lower levels or at a party whose main entertainment are levitating performers who are half-dragon, half-human. What has been provided that you can employ to good effect?

Pitfalls

Sometimes when you go to put these stories down on paper, they are not the complete, well-developed entities one might hope for, but incomplete things, hints of lines instead of the entire picture, whispers instead of words, a sense of brushing up against one side of the story in the dark rather than holding it in its entirety. In such cases, I usually build a mind-map, writing down the details that I know and expanding from that. I'll build on how to do that in the Next Steps section.

Be careful of the generic. We all have a set of flimsy and

unconvincing stage sets in our heads that, when examined with care, can be traced back to specific television shows or movies. My desert island will always have Gilligan lurking in the underbrush, for example, and any Victorian London scenes have to be forcibly wrenched out of the black and white of the old Basil Rathbone Sherlock Holmes movies.

Next steps

Take your two or three sentence description and expand on it, stretching it to five hundred words by expanding on generic details with specifics and figuring out the overall timeline.

I map things out in a large sketchbook, writing the details I know in the center and filling in details as they occur to me: house → Victorian mansion → decrepit, ghost in old greenhouse.

Write out the overall list of scenes then develop the basic beats of what happens in each scene: they go to the movies, see a clue in the opening, and try to rush out of the theater only to find a bunch of lamias in the parking lot ready to brawl; they fight with the lamias and defeat them by throwing soap bombs at them, but Ellen's arm gets broken in the process. You will probably tell it in chronological order, but it's not too early to think about mixing it up if you think it would accomplish something in the story, like provide additional pleasure for the reader by allowing them to assemble the pieces of the puzzle.

Exercises

1. More about that beat thing. I'm borrowing this concept from the book *Hamlet's Hit Points: Unlock the Gamemastering Power of Three Classic Tales* by Robin D. Laws. Laws is talking about writing for games, but the book has some light to shed on storytelling in general and I highly recommend it.
2. Laws breaks stories down into separate moments, or beats. Each beat either changes or reinforces the audience's understanding of things, and move the reader towards either hope or fear. A beat can do things like affect emotion, provide information, give a

reader a chance to savor something, provide a question or answer, but no matter what, it generally moves the story along.

3. Laws analyzes three narratives: Hamlet, Dr. No, and Casablanca in a way that is revelatory and well worth the read (doing so first is the overachiever's version of this exercise). But with or without the benefit of having read it, go through and identify the procedural and dramatic moments in your story. What needs to happen to move your protagonist along? What moments will be used to increase your reader's identification with the character?
4. Find the list of what some people perceive as the seven basic plots on Wikipedia. Write a quick story synopsis with three distinct characters, using one of the plots as a model. Overachiever version: do all seven with the same characters.

Case study: (Pippa's Smiles)

The first study is "Pippa's Smiles," which originally appeared in *Daily Science Fiction*. I woke up one morning with the plot fairly complete in my head: a man, discontented with his wife and home life, sets off in search of adventure and finally returns home, ready now to be happy with his existence, only to find it is no longer an option.

In thinking about the story, I wanted to think about the other side of the traditional story of a hero going forth and meeting three challenges. I didn't know what form the challenges would take, but I did know that there had to be three of them all together. And because I was thinking about the gendered implications of the traditional story, where women serve as goals or rewards, I made each of the encounters be one with femininity, but each time a female force that really doesn't care about the protagonist, to the point where the last one utterly ignores him.

And then he returns to something—someone—he had taken for granted. That's the emotional core of this story, at least how I'd describe it: sometimes you can feel a lack and let it drive you on an outer quest, when what you really need is an inner self-examination.

With that understanding in my head, I sat down and wrote this over the course of a few hours, letting the encounters define themselves by writing and seeing what happened. I knew the ending already, so I could easily go back, once I had finished the draft, and tweak the beginning so it set up theat ending in a satisfactory way by referencing the smiles and the pearls.

Pippa's Smiles

Marcus hadn't thought marriage would be like this after three months. He had expected to love her, but he hadn't thought she would love him so much, that she would follow him from counter to till in his tiny shop where he sold souvenirs and curiosities: stuffed mermaids, filigree jars, and great shark jaws set with more teeth than a carved comb.

Was it that he was all the treasure that Pippa had? Would her need diminish with time, as she felt more secure?

His mother had wanted him to marry Gerta the innkeeper's daughter, who could run a household with easy efficiency, could scald a hog or bleach linen, and who had wide hips that could bear a score of infants. His father had wanted him to marry Lisa the banker's daughter, who came with a hefty dowry and land of her own, and who had wide hips that could bear two score infants. Maybe more.

But he had seen narrow-hipped Pippa the day she'd arrived in the seaport town of Spume, in the pinnacle that had rescued all that remained of a capsized galleon: Pippa in her drenched skirts and two sailors, one with a scar across his eye and the other a rangy man with only one hand who claimed that a kraken had eaten the other.

The sailors had moved on quickly, taken other ships, but Pippa had stayed behind when Marcus had asked her to become his bride, enchanted by her small, brown-skinned form, her dandelion fluff of hair, her mismatched eyes, one sea foam green, the other as blue as summer sky, the tiny smile that she only let escape in moments of true delight, and which she kept clutched inside at all other times.

She loved him too. At night, she touched him, laying her hand along his back, to make sure he wasn't dead. They were both light sleepers. Wakened by some outside sound—the last of the late night drunkards stumbling home from the tavern in the next street, the cobblestone clatter of a cart, or the apothecary's dog barking at some imagined monster – they would both lie there for a moment. And then Pippa would turn over and lay her hand on his back or side, feeling for his warmth, and then, reassured, would go back to sleep.

It was because she feared losing him, he knew. It wasn't easy but he hadn't expected marriage to be easy. He knew he was a man set in his own ways. His own mother said, "Marcus was a grown man before he was ever a boy." He had followed a different path than his farmer father, had been lured to become a shopkeeper, though not just any shopkeeper. He did not sell merchants' doings, but the odd things sailors brought from other shores, which had fascinated him since he was a boy, and had first seen a gleam of porcelain luck-beads in a traveler's palm, offered for a bag of apples.

To Pippa, he was a greater treasure than anything in the shop. She'd sit watching him as he dusted, telling her each item's name and making her repeat it to him in her soft, slurry accent. He taught her names of spices that were rarely used in local cooking and the adjective for each historical dynasty's antiques, and left her to pick up the simpler things on her own, like "salt" and "water" and "bread."

She rarely left his side in the shop, but would sit there, weaving lace and watching him with those bright eyes. Sometimes she was so pretty he could not help but come and kiss her, and then she would give him a little smile, brighter than any coin. It worried him that she only gave him those smiles. In front of his parents, he'd coax and joke, hoping to elicit one, hoping that she'd show them why he loved her so, but she hoarded them and would only spend them when they were alone together.

Alone together, and never alone, truly alone, by himself. She was always there. He felt suffocated. He grew impatient. He tried to hide, to catch a breath to himself. But she followed him, bright-eyed and curious, even in the most private moments. He wondered what she saw when she looked at him, what her eyes saw, to make her love him so.

It was too much. It was all together too much.

And so he waited until he saw her drinking the willowbark tea that she took to relieve the ache of her courses. That way he knew she was not with child, for he didn't want to leave her that way. He made love to her that night despite her protest, for he did want to remember her that way, with a wondering smile on her face. And he did not look back in the morning, because he didn't want to remember her that way, bewildered and crying, clutching the key to the shop in her hand.

He took a backpack of clothes and a stout walking stick and a purseful of coins he'd meant to use to buy pearls when Jacobo, a favorite sailor, passed through again. And he went out into the world to escape the love that weighed on him so unexpectedly. His mother had not loved his father so, although they were the best of friends. He had thought that was how his own marriage would be patterned, that it would not come to resemble a yoke around his neck.

He had walked for a month and a day, and seen more wonders than he could count, when he came to a pool beside the road where a waterfall spilled out on great green boulders, which churned the surface into milky foam. He saw naiads splashing in the water, and they waved to him with long, languid arms, their blue hair spilling out around them like weeds, and sang to him, a sweet and unknown song whose meaning he could only guess at.

He had meant to remain true to his wife, for he would not have it said he had been fickle and left her for another woman. But the song called him, and he laid his pack and staff down beside the pool (and hid his purse underneath a stone, for he was a prudent man), and dove in.

But there the women seemed not to notice his presence. He swam down, down in the water and there on the pool's floor he saw skeletons, skulls gaping up at him and grinning at the joke that he might join them. He felt hair drifting around his ankles, his wrists, soft and fine but strong as rope. He panicked and swam upwards despite their pull, and when he broke the surface he clambered gasping onto the bank, blue strands still clinging to his ankles.

The naiads shrugged and combed each other's hair as he walked away. Far below their song, the skulls continued grinning.

The road wore him down. It cracked his heels and sifted dust into the seams of his clothing, so he could not wash it out, no matter how he tried. He began to think longing thoughts of his shop, of Pippa leaving his side long enough to make him tea and bring it to him, hot and sweet as he preferred it. He thought of the lace she wove and how many yards she must have finished in his absence.

He wondered if Jacobo had brought the pearls he promised and if Pippa had reluctantly turned him away, or whether she had managed to scrape together enough coin to buy them. They would have proved a good investment, because merchants' wives loved pearls, and claimed them tokens of true love.

He wondered why he never thought of Lisa or Marta when remembering that vanished life. Only Pippa. And even now, the thoughts made him feel that he was being smothered – or drowned – overwhelmed with the love that she no doubt still held, hoping he would come back.

He thought he would, when he was done walking. But he'd teach her to be independent, to spend time without him. He'd make her go to his mother and learn to sew, learn to sit in the circle of women and natter as happily as they did, stitching away on their husbands' clothes.

Fog overtook the road one day and he walked in silence, thinking that he heard sounds, footsteps somewhere in the white darkness, accompanying him. He saw faces in the mist, mostly Pippa's face: frowning, yearning, wanting. Never smiling. He thought he heard a scrap of song that took him off the road, and he blundered through the forest, wondering if the wood-wives would come to him, try to make him stay there with them. That was how they reproduced, catching travelers and keeping them, he knew.

He kept watching for a trunk to split, a green-skinned woman emerge to claim him. He was young and strong, and few men walked in the woods here. They must have summoned the fog to snare him, were waiting for him in the cloudy air, waiting for him to discover their hiding place. Surely word had gone out the minute he stepped into their forest: a man, walking, the prize they spent their lives waiting for, arrived at last.

But no trees spoke to him, no arms reached for him, and when he stumbled into daylight, he found himself on the edge of the forest, and back on the road again.

He had walked for another month and a day when he saw the castle far ahead. It sat on a mountaintop, and the road spiraled up to meet its gates. When he knocked there, a guard opened the gate, dressed in gilt and lilac armor, asking what he wanted.

"Whose castle is this?" Marcus asked.

"The Sorceress Alyx," the guard said.

It all made sense now. She had magically summoned him, that was why he had left his wife and come to her. She had glimpsed him, in a scrying mirror or crystal ball, and decided that he would be hers. He would rule in the castle by her side, and see to setting things right. Women had little idea how to govern, and she had probably realized she needed help.

But when Marcus said he had come to see the Sorceress, the guard only laughed, although not in an unkindly way, and said that Marcus might sleep that night in the kitchens, warm and fed, but that the Sorceress held no audiences.

The soup was good and thick, and there were bits of chicken with it, and slices of well-crusted bread, and even a tankard of cider to wash it all down. Full-bellied, Marcus lay down upon the cot he'd been given, but could not sleep.

At least, he dreamed he could not sleep. He would stir, and wait for Pippa's touch on his back, and the little reassured sound she made when she felt him breath. At length he went wandering through the castle, slipping through the hallways unnoticed, for the guards were outside, protecting the castle from those who would enter unlawfully.

He passed tapestries woven of bone and iron, and wonderful things that he would have liked to sell in his shop: hourglasses that told when sunset would occur, and great narwhal horns, and a clockwork woman who told fortunes when you put a coin in her nose. He gave her a coin, and the little pasteboard ticket he received in return said, "She would have waited forever."

He smiled at this assurance and wondered what Pippa was doing, right then. Surely she was sleeping, dreaming of him dreaming of her. Or did the card speak of the Sorceress, and her devotion to him, so strong that she would have waited forever, had he not responded to her call?

He went up a winding staircase and found himself in the sorceress's chamber. She sat there on a high-backed chair, looking out over the land, her golden hair about her like a curtain. He told her he had come, and expected her to turn and smile and greet him, but she ignored him, still looking out the window. He frowned at this. He was the hero of this dream, and she was meant to turn and smile at him.

He thought, "Perhaps she cannot hear me, or perhaps she is shy and wishes me to initiate things." Going to her, he leaned and said in her ear, "I have never kissed a sorceress."

She pushed a button and he was pulled from the room by soldiers. He realized that he was only a nuisance, like a fly buzzing, for she had shown no rancor on her face, only impatience. As though he was interrupting very important business. As they took him away, he saw her lean forward towards the window again, her face intent. She had already forgotten him.

He had been wrong. She was not waiting for him, or any man.

He thought they might imprison him, deep below the castle. But instead them simply put him out the gate, and even gave him back his stick and pack, and a bundle of bread and cheese. He felt small and unimportant, and above all, impatient as he went back down the mountainside. He would return, and Pippa would give him smiles again, and this time he would teach her better and she would learn when he wanted her to stare at him and when he wanted her to leave him alone.

He had walked very far, and it was almost a year before he saw the walls of the seaport again. They glimmered in the sunlight, for the day was fair and bright, as though everything rejoiced to see him returned, to see him back in his proper place. He half ran down the street, past familiar faces that looked startled to see him, and sometimes filled with another emotion that he thought must be envy, that he had gone so far, was so well traveled now, and was returning to his wife, who had no doubt kept things well till his return, and would give him the keys along with another purse of coins, even fatter than the one he had left with.

But when he came to the window of his shop, he looked in. There was Pippa, but not as he expected. She held a baby in her arms and he thought with great regret that he had erred that last night, that he had left her with child despite his efforts. He felt a twinge of guilt and thought, "I'll make it up to her, though." He set his hand to the door knob and then he saw through the cloudy glass, amid the strings of glass balls that are said to hold the souls of witches, illuminated by a lantern carved of ivory and fish bones, amid trinkets and trivialities, the lace upon her shoulders and Jacobo's pearls gleaming around her throat, and Jacobo's arm around her waist, and he realized then, bile biting in his throat, that she would never spend her smiles on him again.

Chapter 2
TECHNIQUE

What it is

A technique is a rhetorical device that you decide you want to apply. Usually it's either something that you've noticed in someone else's writing or a concept, sometimes from another branch of art, that you've been reading about and that you want to explore.

As an example of the latter, I noticed when I first started reading Joe Abercrombie's work how he handled transitions. The ending of a chapter would reference something like falling snow, for example, and then that snow would appear again at the beginning of the next chapter, but with a totally different perspective.

In writing "Grandmother", I decided to do something similar because I wanted to test it out. Here's that section in action:

> *The flyer shuddered and moved. They both looked forward towards the parade's bustle, but Gareth stole one more glance.*

Her profile looked like one from a coin, pale blue against the silvery sky, the shimmer of the water-repelling shield. He felt a surge of admiration.

She didn't care much whether or not he was here, though. The person she'd be looking for during the parade would be...

...her daughter was usually here on these occasions, Phoenix thought. She missed Ruby. But the girl—if she could still call her that, when her daughter was pushing seventy—had sent word that she could not make this Founding Day, though she regretted it.

As you can see, it's used to swing us through a scene break that switches point of view within the same scene. Gareth looks at Phoenix and thinks that she is watching for someone / break / we move into Phoenix's point of view and discover it is her daughter. I still think it's a nifty little movement, and I tried out a couple of other techniques in this story, such as the repeated "They said" in the beginning.

Before doing something with a specific technique, I try to think about what the technique achieves and what it gives the story. I will find and dissect examples of it and see what they have in common. Once I think I understand how it works, I sit down and write something and see what happen

What it provides

This is a starting point that can give you a great deal, but probably doesn't give you a lot. With the example from "Grandmother," I knew that I would want the same side character to be the transition, so I needed to think of two other characters that related to her, and then work backward from that, putting the first section in Gareth's point of view and the second in Phoenix's.

That triangle of character dynamics helped opened up the complete picture: a mother/daughter struggle, and the mother's hapless lover as a pawn in that. I wanted it to be space opera, and I borrowed some touches from a space opera-ish construction I'd created as part of a group storytelling exercise on an early BBS (Note, created by Greg Travis at Indiana University), mainly Phoenix's appearance, her occupation, and the name of her ship, The Black Thechu.

Your mileage here will vary greatly accordingly, and I suggest trying to figure out how the technique you want to try maps to one of the other starting points, such as character, plot, scene, etc, and factor that in as well.

Considerations

You need to figure out what you don't have and start fleshing that out.

If it's a plot, think about how the technique might echo it. Is it something where you're playing with word confusions? Then is there a plot that could revolve around that: a quest posed by an ancient riddle, two translators working together on a peace treaty that will end an interstellar war, a futuristic advertising executive who must come up with the perfect cola campaign or face ritual death in the arena?

Does what you're using give you characters? If not, what kind of characters might it imply? Again, can you create and capitalize on some echo between the technique and your cast? A technique or device works best when there is a reason to be using it. It should contribute something to the narrative with its existence other than showing how clever the writer is. If you have character(s), you can try to extrapolate a plot outward by figuring out what they want and what's thwarting them. If you are working with multiple characters, it's best if they are somehow thwarting each other.

Does what you're using give you a world? You know the drill by now: what clever echoes and reverberations can you create by supplying a setting that somehow interacts with the technique?

Or you can start with the emotional core—is there one that somehow works with your technique? Let's go back to the idea of a technique involving word confusion (Examples: regular occurrences of puns, references to poems in an alien language, a character who is constantly quoting aphorisms incorrectly). Is there something a story can say about such confusion or deception? For example:

- It's possible to misunderstand people and have it go horribly awry.
- Confusions can lead to heartbreak if you don't speak directly.
- Sometimes confusions can lead to good results.
- In doing so, remember that sometimes finding a core takes some time and (often unconscious) mulling.

Pitfalls

It's possible that you just don't have enough to go on. You want to write something in blank verse, but you can't figure out a reason to. Unless you're under a deadline, you may want to put this one away in the cellar of your mind and let it ripen. This is a perfectly reasonable and justifiable thing to do, but if it's a habit you acquire, you need to pick up a second habit as well: wandering through that cellar to tap the various ideas to see if any sound ready to slice open again.

More likely something will prompt you to go back to the idea. You'll get an idea and think, Oh, now's the time to test out that technique in a story. Test it out; it may or may not work, but often this organic approach will work better than forcing a story into draft form. That's not to say you can't push something in this fashion, but in that case you'd better be ready to sit down and start free-writing and then deal with whatever mess emerges.

Next steps

Figuring out how the technique and your story tie together is key. Until you have that, you are driving without a map and the roads can prove slippery. Pantsing your way into a story with just a technique to guide you is doable, but it's not going to be one of those neat little stories that requires little to no re-writing unless you have gotten very very good at letting your unconscious mind go to work and construct wonders for you to admire.

Examine the technique. Where did it come from and how does its shape reflect that origin? If it's a literary device, does it have an associated history? What sort of impression does it create in a reader's head; what might it remind them of?

Think of three possible stories in which the technique would work against the story, i.e. be a bad choice. What do they have in common? Is there something that seems as though it might be their antithesis? Yes, I am actually saying figure out how to do it badly and then do the opposite. That technique may or may not work for you.

Exercises

1. Find a website or book with a list of rhetorical devices - pick one and figure out a possible plot that would go with it. OA: do three possible plots.
2. Find a book that you have always loved and reread, taking notes as you go. How does the author create the reader's experience? Pick one of their techniques and use it in a passage of your own. OA: write a scene in which two or more of their techniques are combined.
3. This one's tricky. Is there some way your character is related to the device? If it's a repeated phrase, is it something they say, for example, or perhaps something that other people say to them.

Case study: (Kallakak's Cousins)

I started "Kallakak's Cousins" with two things: a technique I wanted to use and a setting for it, a space station I'd written a couple of stories in before, TwiceFar. The technique that I wanted to use was employing physical sensory stuff to get the reader inside the protagonist: Kallakak is dealing with exhaustion as well as a bladder infection as the story begins:

The more annoyed Kallakak got, the sleepier he became. By the time he found himself in the small trapezoidal office that served the Undersecretary of Spaces as a waiting room, weariness washed over him in waves threatening to carry him away into sleep. His mid-hands, which he usually employed for fine work, were shaking with fatigue. He slapped open a pouch and took out a syringe with an upper hand to jab into the opposite arm's pit, preferring that to the soft underside of his stumpy tail's base. He grunted once as the needle pierced the thick skin, and felt the chrome-edged wake-up shock through his nervous system.

The rustle of the space station's ventilating fans sharpened to a whine as the wake-up's second component jolted his metabolism. The only bad side-effect was his bladder's tightening, a yank on his nerves that made him wonder how far away the nearest eliminatory was. He allowed himself to feel gratitude for the lack of caff as his breathing and heartbeat slowed from the initial jolt.

In writing, I ended up applying another set of irritations, this time mental: not just the three feckless cousins who've shown up on Kallakak's doorstep, and who he feels obligated to help, but also the group who want to purchase his shop. What's the heart of the story? That the things that irritate us may save us, perhaps, at least in the cousin' case.

I didn't know the ending till I came to it, and it's a bit facile, in my opinion. If I were writing the story nowadays, I think I might push to find something a little less expected, or at least signal the solution less overtly by complicating the situation with Kallakak's errant wife a little and playing with those expectations.

Kallakak's Cousins

The more annoyed Kallakak got, the sleepier he became. By the time he found himself in the small trapezoidal office that served the Undersecretary of Spaces as a waiting room, weariness washed over him in waves threatening to carry him away into sleep. His mid-hands, which he usually employed for fine work, were shaking with fatigue. He slapped open a pouch and took out a syringe with an upper hand to jab into the opposite arm's pit, preferring that to the soft underside of his stumpy tail's base. He grunted once as the needle pierced the thick skin, and felt the chrome-edged wake-up shock through his nervous system.

The rustle of the space station's ventilating fans sharpened to a whine as the wake-up's second component jolted his metabolism. The only bad side-effect was his bladder's tightening, a yank on his nerves that made him wonder how far away the nearest eliminatory was. He allowed himself to feel gratitude for the lack of caff as his breathing and heartbeat slowed from the initial jolt.

The light was set to an annoying wavelength that scraped angrily at his eyes. Somewhere down the corridor someone kept walking back and forth, a metallic echo of footsteps. Three or four rooms away, he thought, and wondered whose waiting area they had been put in.

"Mr. Kallakak?" a woman said from the doorway, her voice officious and too loud to his tender ears. He flattened the frills atop his head, a rude gesture, but it dampened the noise's edge. She probably didn't know Ballabel etiquette anyway.

Unfortunately, her expression said she did. She said nothing, just turned and gestured him to follow. They traversed a winding corridor up several floors and into the Undersecretary of Spaces' office, where the Undersecretary and two other humanoids awaited him.

"Mr. Kallakak, is it?" the Undersecretary asked, glancing at the pad on his desk for confirmation before Kallakak could reply.

"It's a great pleasure," Kallakak said, preparing to launch into the speech he'd prepared, but the man simply pointed him to a stool.

The Undersecretary wore no uniform, which made Kallakak hope for a moment that he was a long-timer, someone whose position in things as far as the government was concerned remained the same, and didn't shift with every change of the government. But the official's hair was growing out of a military crew-cut, about two weeks worth. Kallakak resigned himself to another iteration of the negotiation for his shop's location that he had undergone, by his count, thirteen times so far.

The room's two other occupants sat quietly. Both were burly and broad-shouldered, with the look of people who had grown up in substantial gravity. Their augmentations were utilitarian, with no pretense towards naturalness: thick metal ridges protected their eyes and laser lenses set over the eyes shifted with the light as they moved. Dark blue plating layered over their arms. Kallakak did not doubt that there were other, more dangerous additions on their forms.

"The Jellidoos here say that they have a prior claim to the space where your shop is located," the Undersecretary said.

Startled by the bluntness, Kallakak looked to the pair. They stared back, expressionless. He had prided himself on his ability to understand shifts in human expression – it was of great value to him in negotiations with customers – but these two were unreadable to him. A wave of torpor washed over him, but he would not inject himself here and show them information about the angry terror their assertion had inspired.

"I have been there three standard years," he said. "What is the prior claim?"

"They have been offstation and thought that their representative was occupying the space," the Undersecretary said. "Their claim dates back four standard years."

"They had no way of checking on their claim?" he said politely.

"Our representative deceived us," the woman said. "Now we have returned in person to take up our merchandising effort again."

"It is a very small and oddly shaped space," Kallakak said. "Surely fine beings like yourselves have access to significantly grander locations?" He looked to the Undersecretary. "Or perhaps such might be found?" He wished the Undersecretary had met him alone; it would be easier to find out how much bribe was needed.

"Despite spatial difficulties, it is a premium location," the woman said. "Just above the Midnight Stair and across from the Convention Hall."

Kallakak nodded to assert his command of human gestures. "May I ask what type of merchandise you intend to sell?"

"Much the same merchandise that you currently sell," she said. She permitted a smile to cross her lips. "We would be glad to give you a good price on your current stock."

He let his eyes slit to demonstrate annoyance while he thought frantically. Would it be best – or even possible --to take his loss and see about finding another location, build up merchandise stocks again?

It would be laborious to clear his things out and re-establish a new shop: across from the Convention Hall was, as he and the other merchants knew full well, a location rivaled only by the entrance to the University or the booths immediately by the port, where every sailor and traveler had to pass. He did not think any other location he could afford would let him stay afloat. Sooner or later, his capital would dwindle bit by bit and destitution would come knocking at his door.

"Will the matter be examined before a court?" he asked, and caught the twitch that might signify the Undersecretary's hope to have avoided the formalities. But the official only said "Yes, of course." Pulling open a window on his desk, he studied it. "The next opening is..."

"We would prefer to have it done quickly," the female Jellimak said, and the official continued on as though he had not heard her, "five days from now."

That was astonishingly quick, and Kallakak wondered if the two realized it. They stood and Kallakak remained in his chair, hoping to speak to the Undersecretary alone. But they continued standing looking at him until at last he resigned himself to exiting with them and rose to his feet in turn. All three bowed to the Undersecretary before leaving.

Outside, the Jellidoos fell in step with him, one on either side, as he walked towards the lift.

"We realize this is an inconvenience for you," the woman said. "We are prepared to offer you compensation for the trouble it causes."

"How much?" he said, tapping the lift call.

"Five thousand standard credits," she said.

While substantial, it was not enough to make up for the space's loss, which netted him that much again every few months. He grunted noncommittally.

"Sometimes we don't realize that what we want isn't good for us," the man said, speaking for the first time. He stared intently at Kallakak.

"Dominance rituals do not work well on me," Kallakak said, roughening his voice to rudeness. "I will see you in five days in the court." He decided not to burn his bridges too far. "I will tally up the cost of my goods by then and will have a definite figure." Let them think him acquiescent while he tried to find another way to save his shop. He stepped into the lift, but they did not follow him, simply watched as the doors slid closed and he was carried away.

Making his way back to his quarters, he saw three figures standing before it. He paused, wondering if the Jellidoos had decided to lean on him further. The trio turned in unison to face him, and he recognized them with a sinking heart. The cousins.

Kallakak had come to TwiceFar space station ten standards earlier with his wife, Akla. Both were Balabels of good family; their births had been normal and each's twin had gone on to a respectable mate and business of their own.

But Akla had a set of cousins who had been born not in a pair but a disreputable and unlucky triad. Moreover, they had continued to stay together long past their adolescence and therefore never matured into sexuality. Not unheard of, certainly, but unusual.

They had not been successful in business and Kallakak had grown used to hearing Akla's stories about their efforts. At times she had been quite witty about it but without her presence to remind him of their existence, he realized he had lost track of them. He had not seen them since he and Akla had joined together, back on Balabel, but he recognized them: they were oddly graduated in size, not the same height, and had a peculiar slump-shouldered appearance.

The tallest – what was its name? – approached Kallakak.

"You may not remember me, sir," it fluted at him, its voice uncertain. "I am Tedesla, and these are my siblings, Desla and Sla. We are related to your wife, Akla."

"She's gone," he said roughly. The corridor lights buzzed brittly behind his head. He could feel a continuing push at his bladder, despite the several eliminatories he'd visited on the way home.

The cousins exchanged glances and conferred in whispers as he waited. He heard the smallest, Sla, say "But we have nowhere else to go!" and reluctantly took pity on them.

"Come inside," he said.

They followed after him, crowding the narrow room that served him as eating and sleeping quarters as well as a warehouse of sorts. Double layers of mesh crates were stacked up against one wall and others had been assembled to create the furniture.

A bed made from a pallet of rugs covered with film plastic sat near two metal boxes pushed together to make a table. He pulled a tab on a caff box, setting it to Heat and put it on the table before rummaging for cups in a box of chipped mugs showing the station's logo. Glancing at the cousins, he grabbed for dried meat as well and opened it.

Two cousins sat on the floor, interspersing rapid bites of meat with gulps of caff, while Sla did the same, cross-legged on the bed, its bones still adolescent soft and flexible. Kallakak averted his eyes and focused on Tedesla.

"We won a prize," Tedesla said. "A ticket for all three of us to the station."

"A prize?"

"For our shopping, for being the 1,000,000th customer at the new grocer's."

"A prize for shopping?" Kallakak considered the idea. It would be easy enough to do something similar with his shop – if he still had it after five days, he thought sourly. He bit into a meat stick, looking at Tedesla.

"How much money is left?" he said.

Tedesla shrugged. "That's all it was, a ticket."

"And one to go back on?"

"No." Tedesla hesitated. "It was supposed to be round trip for two but there were three of us. So there is a trip back for one."

"Which one?"

They shrugged in perfect unison. As though evoked by the gesture, he felt the day come crashing down on him, sleep crawling over his skin like an insect swarm.

"You can stay until we get things settled," he grunted. Setting his cup down, he moved over to the bed, Sla scrambling out of his way. He laid down with his back to them and fell downwards into sleep.

In the morning, he saw they had tidied away the food from the night before. He thought they might have gone exploring, but when he pushed the corridor door open, he found them sitting outside in the hallway. They rose to their feet.

"I am going to the store," he said. "Have you seen it already?" They shook their heads and followed him.

"I named it 'Akla's Wares,'" he told them as he walked along. "I stock the things she liked: Corrinti bubbles and other sparkles, things tourists buy."

"She liked such things?" Sla asked.

"She does," he said.

They turned the corridor and headed up the Midnight Stair, moving along handholds rather than taking the stairs, the gravity feather light around them. Kallakak's muscular arms moved him along more rapidly than the majority of pedestrians along the hundred meter wide tunnel, its sides lined with black stairs that showed no sign of scuff or wear.

"It wasn't smooth going at first," Kallakak said. "Twice I got robbed during sleep periods, so I hired a mechanical to run it while I wasn't there."

"A mechanical?" Tedesla asked.

"A robot," Kallakak said. "Most of them are trying to buy themselves or others free, they take on whatever labor they can manage. Alo2 is a good sort. Funny sense of humor, but a good sort."

"We could watch over the shop," Sla said. "With us here, you wouldn't need anyone else."

He didn't answer, but paused in the doorway of the pharmacist. "The usual," he snapped at Ercutio, who replied as he passed over the pack of juice bulbs, "If you wouldn't retain your fluids in your body so much, they would not cause the infection."

He ran his card through the reader to pay. "I know, I know," he said.

"Who are those with you?" Ercutio nodded at the cousins, who stood backing Kallakak in a little ring.

"Cousins," he said. He toothed through the seal of a juice bulb and sucked down the salty-sweet fluid, mixed with antibiotics.

"I heard there's some trouble with your space," Ercutio said and Kallakak paused before hurrying out of the doorway. "Some," he said. "I'll know more in a day or so, need to size things up."

They moved along towards the shop. The name "Akla's Wares", written in standard and red Balabel script rode the wall above the doorway, which Kallakak had widened at his own expense in order to make it easier for customers to enter.

Alo2 looked at them from where he sat beside the counter.

"We are Kallakak's cousins. You will no longer be needed," Sla told the mechanical in an officious tone.

Kallakak hastened to say "Don't listen to it. Visitors from home. Go look at the merchandise, you three, while I catch up."

Alo2 registered the knowledge with a flicker of the blue lenses that served it as eyes. Its surface was matte steel, marred in places with dents from years at dock labor. "The shop took in 541 standards," it said. "A party of six sailors bought twelve souvenir items at 2:11. Two Jellidoos came by but bought nothing."

"Did they say anything to you?" he asked.

"They wanted to know the sum of my wages," Alo2 said. "I misrepresented them as considerably more than I make."

"Good," Kallakak said enviously. He was incapable of lying; the effort of it caused a purpling of the ear frills that was unmistakable to anyone knowing much of Balabel physiology. While a master of understatement and misdirection, he envied Alo2's ability to overtly misstate things.

"Jellidoos are tough to deal with," Alo2 said in a statement of absolute truth and Kallakak nodded in glum agreement.

"They used to use a lot of mechanicals," Alo2 said.

"Used to?"

"They're superstitious. We spread a rumor that mechanicals hold souls that have been displaced from bodies – ghosts. Not all of us, mind you, just a few. They're terrified of ghosts and death."

"Too bad we can't convince them this place was once a body repository or something," Kallakak said. He looked around at the walls, which were a dull layer of cloudy plastic over gray metal.

It was unclear what use the station's creators had meant to put the space to centuries ago. Finding it unused except for storage, Kallakak had submitted petitions to three versions of TwiceFar's constantly changing government, achieving success on the fourth try. He touched the counter, a silvery glass slab he'd found in a cast-off sale at the University and swore.

"What?" Alo2 asked.

"I've put too much work into this to see it taken away," he said, feeling tired. "It is the only thing I have to remember Akla by. It is her past—my future.

He turned to the cousins. "All right. Desla, sweep the back aisles, Sla, wash the wall – you'll want to unpin those scarves first and then put them back up. Tedesla, sort that box of mail cards, and make sure they're grouped together by language. Alo2, can you stay a few more hours and show Tedesla how to operate the credit reader?"

"Where are you going?" Sla asked.

"To do some research."

"Huh," Bo said after he'd listened to the whole long saga. "Jellidoos are bad news; they know law inside and out."

"You'd think that they wouldn't know TwiceFar law," Kallakak said bitterly. He took a sip from the fragrant tea Bo had served him, redolent with yellow, straw-like flowers that smelled like honey and apple.

"They've probably been waiting for a turn that would allow them to do this," Bo said. His height had been augmented to over two meters and that, coupled with his ferocious black eyes, helped him keep his own establishment orderly. "A lot of people watch the station to see how things change, watching for opportunities. But how can they claim your space? I thought it was unoccupied until you moved in there."

"It was," Kallakak said. "But there was a caff cart stored there for three days at one point, a temporary measure. They are claiming occupation based on having owned most of the cart."

"Feh," Bo said. "So you can make it too expensive for them to force you out, I suppose..."

"Hard to do. In that location, they can recoup a very large sum quickly. Larger than I can raise against them."

"You can wait them out and see what happens next time the government shifts."

Kallakak shook his head. "Then they'll have been the most recent occupants – most law will lie in their favor."

"It's a shame," Bo said. "I remember when you arrived – took you a year to save up enough to buy citizenship, let alone start to make claim to that space. When you and your wife first came..." The sentence trailed off in awkward silence.

"All done and gone," Kallakak said. He drank the last of his tea, now cool.

Back at the shop, he swore when he saw the mess Sla had created. The scarves, draped against a wall still damp from washing, had bled mottled dyes onto the wall's plastic.

"I didn't mean to," it said, shrinking unhappily into itself. Tedesla came up behind it and touched its shoulder, giving Kallakak a look that reminded him of Akla. By the end, she had learned to play his guilt-strings like a musical instrument. The emotion glittered in his mind like Sla's unhappy eyes.

"It doesn't matter," he sighed. "Take those down and fold them. We'll sell them to the Jellidoos for a decent sum, I'm sure." He frowned at the colored wall; the pink and green dye had left pale, feathery patterns like fern leaves.

Late that night, he heard them whispering together, admonishing Sla. After they finished, he heard the smallest cousin weeping and then the other two comforting it.

"Of course it is strange here," Desla said. "But tomorrow we will go and get the little cream pastries from the Food Court that the woman was talking about. Sweet and light as air, she said."

"We'll bring some back," Desla murmured. "He deserves to be taken care of, now that he no longer has his wife."

"He never speaks of her," observed Tedesla.

"Never," said Sla. "Do you think she died of something gruesome?" The other two shushed it and lapsed into murmurs that he couldn't make out.

When the hallway lights brightened to morning shift white, he let the increased angstroms tug his eyelids awake and drank another of the sour bulbs. His bladder felt much the same as it had the day before, irritated and a little sore, but at least it was no worse.

Sla was cheerful. Kallakak gave the three the day free, with a handful of coupons and vouchers he had gathered through exchanges with other merchants.

Alo2 was sweeping out the aisles as he entered.

"Where's your entourage?" it asked. He shook his head. "Sent the pack of them off to the Food Court."

"Good. What are you going about the Jellidoos?"

"There's not much I –can– do," he said. Moving over to the card-reader, he tapped at it, checking the totals. "I'm going to see the Undersecretary today. Can you watch over the shop again?"

"And the cousins?" the mechanical said.

He shook his head. "I told them they were off today and to meet me at evening to eat together."

"They tried to ask me questions about Akla yesterday."

"What did you say?"

"That I didn't know anything. I think they don't understand that non Ballabel can lie yet. Not that I'm complaining. I had the middle one fetching and carrying for me yesterday when I described the pain that sudden movements caused to my resistors."

He laughed. "They'll learn soon enough, I'm sure." He drank another juice bulb, feeling his outlook improving. His cheer was confirmed when the Undersecretary saw him with surprising promptness, but the emotion fled when the official bluntly mentioned the sum the Jellidoos had already provided.

"I can't match that in the short term," Kallakak ventured. "But perhaps over the course of time..."

The official shook his head. "Things change too quick around here. There hasn't been a government that's lasted more than six months in over a decade," he said. "Who's to say what could happen? Better to grab what I can while I can."

"All right," Kallakak said.

Bo was similarly discouraging. "Chimp down in the Click Bar said the Undersecretary picks up lonely sailors every once in a while, treats them to a good meal and usually breakfast too, isn't too picky about looks. I don't have anyone that could lean on him."

"And the Jellidoos are better at brute force leaning anyhow," Kallakak said. He sighed. "Thanks anyway."

Coming home through the Food Court, he came across a noodle vendor screaming at the cousins, who stood in a line before the livid, red-faced man, their upper and midhands clasped together in embarrassment.

"What's happened here?" he asked, hurrying up.

"They pick up soup unit, get it all mixed around, bad programming!" the man yelled, his voice grating across Kallakak's ears. "Expensive machine!"

"We were just looking at it," Sla said sullenly, its tail lashing.

"We thought that you might get one for the shop," Desla said.

"How much to fix?" Kallakak said to the merchant. He wished he could lie, wished he could pretend this trio, so clearly linked to him, were of no relation, no consequence to him. But their every moment proclaimed them his.

"Fifty credits."

"Give you ten here and now or twenty store credit."

"Fifteen here and now." The merchant swiped Kallakak's card through his reader, punching in the numbers as he eyed the cousins. As though his money wasn't flowing away rapidly enough, he thought.

"You're not paying him, are you?" Sla asked. "We were just looking!"

"Apparently you punched a few buttons," Kallakak said tiredly. They followed him as he circled around the entrance of the Midnight Stair, towards the shop.

"You could sell a lot of food in your shop," Sla said.

"We aren't zoned to sell food."

"But you sell the chocolate and fruit boxes."

"Those are sealed."

"Oh," Sla said.

"Tonight you can watch over the store with Alo2," he said. "First two of you in a five hour shift, then Desla by itself."

"All right," Tedesla said agreeably.

"What will I do by myself?" Desla asked, alarmed.

"You can go sit in the shop with them. You just won't be working. Although if you get bored, Alo2 can show you how to weave hiber baskets. We sell a lot of those."

"And what will we do when Desla is working?" Tedesla asked. "Sit and weave baskets as well?"

"You may also wish to go and fetch yourselves some food at that point, and perhaps bring some back for Desla. In such a case, do not look at or touch any machines, but allow the vendor to hand you the food," he said. "At any rate, I will see you in the morning."

But in the solitude of the room, things felt empty. Much as they had after Akla's departure, full of strange echoes and spaces that could not be filled with boxes of Corrinti jellies and bioluminescent inks. He drank another bulb of medicinal juice and chewed his way through a pack of dried protein flakes, washing them down with swallows of meaty, buttery tea, while his midhands spread lotion on each other, brushing away bits of accumulated, over grown skin and picking away the cuticle in order to burnish each sharp, curved claw.

"I do miss you," he said aloud to the empty air. "I do."

The next day, Desla managed to flood the shop. All three had had digestive problems due to an excess of cream pastries and the eliminatory near the shop had overloaded and backed up. He waded through an expanse of dirty water, opening the shop door to see more water pooling in the aisles, bearing on its surface a film of dust, lint, and scraps of packing material. He turned the water off at its source and sent for a registered plumber before setting the trio to mopping. They carried the water, four dirty buckets at a time, to the recycler so he could reclaim at least some of the fee.

"Look," he said to Tedesla. "The three of you might look around for another job. I will lose the shop in three days to others with a prior claim, and I will not have anything for you to do."

"We can do that." Tedesla said. It patted his arm kindly. "Do not worry, Akla's husband. We will help provide for the household, and keep you in the style which she would have wished."

"That's not what I meant," he said. "I mean, I will have an excess of goods and no place to put them while I look for more shop space. The room will be quite full."

Tedesla's ear frills quivered eloquently with disappointment, but all he said was "I see" before he went back to helping mop the water from the floor.

In between researching ways to save the shop, he tried to find them living space, but there was an influx of visitors – a trade market was being held within the next three days and so he resigned himself to another week of their presence. He kept them on a schedule opposite his own, pointing out its efficiency in keeping the store constantly open, and paid Alo2 double the usual wages to keep an eye on them.

Meanwhile he found a private access unit and searched through endless datanets, trying to find a legal loophole in between constant trips to the eliminatory to soothe the burning in his groin. He stopped on the way home for more bulbs and ignored Ercutio's questions. Every search had closed another door. When he got to the store, he found Bo waiting with advice.

"One of the new employees came from a Jellidoo background so I asked them about the culture," he said to Kallakak. "You need to be careful of what you say to them. Their specialty is libel and slander, and they'll provoke you into saying anything that you can possibly be sued for."

"As though taking the store were not bad enough?" Kallakak grumbled.

"Rumor says we might be in for a governmental tumble," Bo said.

"So soon?"

"This has been a pretty apathetic government; a lot of old-timers aren't too happy with it."

"But still, if it were to change within two days, that would be a quicker change than any I've seen here," Kallakak said.

"True," Bo said, "But I thought the mention of it might cheer you up. How are your new additions doing?"

"They haven't done much so far today," Kallakak said. "Sla tried to eat a tourist's pet last night, apparently, but Alo2 stopped it in time."

Bo snorted.

"They're coming for dinner anytime now," Kallakak said, glancing at the light level in the corridor.

But the next people to come in the door were not the cousins, but rather the pair of Jellidoos. Kallakak smiled politely at them and signaled unobtrusively with a midhand to Bo, who drifted nearer, staring at them.

"We have heard that there have been acts of sabotage in the shop," the man said. The woman pointed at the colors on the back wall. "And water," the man added. "There has been a broken pipe?"

"A small problem, quickly solved," Kallakak said. Sla and the others came through the door just in time to catch the last.

"Is there a problem?" Sla asked. The three came to look at the Jellidoos as well.

"We do not want any more damage to our property," the man said. "We are prepared to offer a sum for immediate vacancy. Or else we will begin charging for damages to what will be our property."

"Never!" Sla said indignantly and behind him, Bo rolled his eyes at Kallakak, mouthing the words "libel and slander".

"You have no right to oust Kallakak! You are very bad people to do so!" Desla added.

"Tell me more," the woman said, listening avidly. "Why should we not oust him?"

"He named this shop after his wife and she remains to watch over it, with love and affection!" Tedesla said despite Kallakak's frantic signal.

Kallakak opened his mouth to correct it, but then shrugged and remained silent.

"How so?" the man demanded. "Do you mean she still lives here?"

"In her death, as in her life, she remains by his side!" Sla declaimed. "Looking after him with eternal devotion."

"A ghost!" the woman exclaimed, paling. She and her compatriot exchanged glances.

"It is a trick," he said, but she shook her head. "Ballabels cannot lie," she said. "See his ear frills?"

Although they could, Kallakak thought, neglect to correct mistaken impressions. Akla had left aboard a freighter, saying that she wanted to "find herself" and had never come back. No sane Ballabel chose a life of solitude, and he had not wanted to correct the cousins in thinking her dead. She would have, he thought, preferred that.

"Will you be withdrawing the claim?" he said to the man as the Jellidoos pushed their way through the cousins towards the door. The woman spat and made a gesture he did not recognize as his only reply.

"Nicely done," Bo said as she exited.

Kallakak beamed at the cousins with effulgent satisfaction. Fumbling behind the counter, he took out an unopened decanter of spirits and fumbled at the stopper.

"So the shop is safe?" Tedesla said.

"Yes," Kallakak said, pouring drams into mugs patterned with glittering stars.

"We don't need to get jobs after all! We can keep working in the shop!" Sla said.

"Well," said Kallakak. "I don't know if I'd go that far."

CHAPTER 3

PREDETERMINED STRUCTURE

What it is

A predetermined structure is the container in which you will put your story. A form is about the shape of things. For example:

- Toby Barlow's werewolf novel in blank verse, *Sharp Teeth*
- Nabokov's *Pale Fire*, told in the form of a poem and its footnotes
- "Wikihistory" by Desmond Warzel, which is the subforum Europe - Twentieth Century - Second World War of the Association of Time Travelers Message Forums

Even if you don't have enough time to look at the books, locating and reading the Wikihistory story will prove both entertaining and instructive.

What it provides

A set of conventions, premade templates that you will fill with your words. This can be a tremendously fun exercise, particularly if you are working with a form that you are very fond of or particularly familiar with (and the more familiar that you are with it, the more you will able to do interesting things with all its interesting facets). Part of the joy in it can be the subversion of the form. For example, Naomi Kritzer's story "So Much Cooking" plays with the form of a recipe blog, and the seriousness of the story combined with the unexpected humor of the form gives the story extra depth.

Structures are also not usually innocent things; they have some history or context behind them. For example:

- Wikipedia entries evolved over the course of the creation of Wikipedia, an early and hugely successful form of crowd-sourcing.
- The sonnet form was introduced by poets Giacomo da Lentini and Dante, and developed by later poets, including Petrarch and Shakespeare. It has a rich history, including famous examples.

Predetermined structures lend themselves well to humor and social satire, but done with the right amount of pathos, they can be extraordinary, as with the Kritzer piece. As with any work where you're trying to mess with the reader's emotions, handle with the same amount of care you would that Jenga piece at the very end of a long game.

Considerations

When I say you have the structure, that is a little deceptive. You will still need to figure out the story arc: how tension rises and is resolved. You have very little of the actual story, in truth, and your best starting point is figuring out what sort of story the structure lends itself to. For example, Wikihistory is told in a series of arguments; go look at some Wikipedia discussion pages and you'll see what I mean. Warzel's used this structure brilliantly, including creating a main character with whom the reader can identify, exasperated SilverFox316, who's just trying to make sure people follow the rules laid out in IATT Bulletin 1147.

What is the flavor created by the conventions and how can you best use it? Is it something highly literary and dry? Is it rude and best suited to something racy or scatalogical (and if so, what happens when you don't use something like that. i.e. a scientist writing about her breakthroughs with genetic engineering in a letter to *Penthouse Magazine*?)

Pitfalls

You cannot think of a reason to use this form. You've thought of something very clever that no one has done before and you want to get it onto the page, but when it comes down to creating the story behind it, you're pulling a blank.

You are having trouble making it new. Google around to see if someone has done it before, whether it's choose your own adventure, a Twitter stream, or a phone app review. But don't get too discouraged if someone has; it's hard to do something new. Try to do more than the first author, to take the idea in unexpected directions that a reader cannot easily predict but is not overly confused by.

Next steps

Study the form that you are using. Read examples of it. Identify what things are a) always contained in it, b) sometimes contained in it, and c) never contained in it.

Think about why you are using it. What does the form bring with it? What will your reader assume about the form and why you're using it? What is being excluded by using the form? What are ways to do something unexpected with it that still fits within its conventions? What speculative possibilities does it present?

Exercises

1. Come up with a list of possible forms (review, guide, menu, letter, encyclopedia article, game instructions). pick one and figure out a possible plot that would go with it. OA: do three possible plots.
2. Think of a written form that you associate with a particular emotion: a newspaper announcement about a wedding (usually happiness), an obituary (sadness), a tax bill (anxiety). Now

write one that creates the opposite emotion; a sad wedding announcement, a happy obit, a complacent tax bill. OA: make it convey both emotions at once.

Case study: (Just the Facts)

I wrote this piece during a session of my Literary Techniques for Genre Writers workshop, after we'd talked about the technique of numbering sections of a story, looking at Kij Johnson's marvelous "26 Monkeys, Also the Abyss". Numbering creates a nice flatness; I also noticed I wanted to make sure I had either ten or twelve steps overall.

Just the Facts

1. There are zombies.
2. Zombies can turn up anywhere. If your mom dies in her sleep, she'll become a zombie that doesn't care whose brain she's (slowly) eating.
3. They are not particularly fast. Some people even poke fun at that. There's a famous web comic called Late Zombies, but has the hero zombie always showing up too late to eat someone.
4. The comic's readership has been declining lately.
5. The web comic creator, seeing the slipping numbers and worrying that her art was becoming stale, has decided to live with zombies for several weeks. She commissioned a plexiglass cage in which to do so, like a shark cage for divers.
6. There's a webcam in the corner of the cubicle, its red eye blinking. Sometimes it seems to blink in time with the zombie footsteps circling, circling, circling the cage.
7. Zombies are boring when they're not chasing you.
8. Zombies can smell blood.
9. The web comic creator has decided to liven things up by letting the zombies around her smell blood. She's cut herself, not too deep, with a pair of scissors she had handy and smeared it on the inside of the plexiglass.
10. Under enough pressure, plexiglass will break.

CHAPTER 4

STEALING

What it is

Sometimes you run into a story where you are just delighted and amazed by the complicated plot. In such a case, you may want to steal it. You are justified in doing so as long as you do it with panache and make it your own. I remind you of Pablo Picasso's words: *Good artists borrow, great artists steal.* By which Picasso meant (I think) that you don't just produce a replica of someone else's work, but take their work and do as you will with it—perhaps even to the point of creating a Burroughs-esque cut-up version of it or perhaps doing that in much smaller and subtler ways, but in either case clearly making it something that you own.

That's okay. As long as you're doing it in order to produce art rather than a profit, in my opinion. But you must genuinely put something of yourself in it. You must add to the mix, not just stir it around. Own it rather than creating an imitation of the original material.

This exercise may, paradoxically, help you refine your understanding of your own style if you spend some time thinking about the process of writing both while writing and afterwards. What feels natural in writing, and what is difficult? Which bits of the story are you particularly proud of? Where did you surprise (or disappoint, but surely not) yourself?

What it provides

Much like plot, stealing gives you a good deal, and it's up to you how thoroughly to rummage through the trunk that you are plundering. It should give you a basic story that you do more with than gluing on some fancy embellishment. If along with the story you are taking setting and characters, you may well be going too far and need to think harder about how you are going to make it your own.

Stealing may give you too much, even; you need to pick and choose among the elements with judicious care, thinking about the effect that you are trying to achieve.

Considerations

It is not okay to borrow people's characters, specific images/words, or worlds without permission. If they are using a character or world drawn from history, you can use it too, but yours must be different. It is okay to borrow plots and this is where you must start. Describe the plot in two or three sentences. That should give you the basics of your action.

How are your characters and world different from the original versions? What flavors and textures are you adding? What do you want to change, improve upon, twist and subvert?

What is it about the source material that you love and want to celebrate? Conversely, are there things about it that you hate or that make you uncomfortable in some way? If it's an older piece, you may want to think about how to make it feel more modern.

How recognizable do you want the source material to be? This is not to be confused with "I want to file all the marks off this so I can plagiarize it successfully." How much do you want your reader to be in on the game and what does it add (or subtract) to read your piece with that source material at hand?

Pitfalls

Does your story read like something the original writer could have written? Then you need to add more of your own special, idiosyncratic, wonderful self. Your piece must be obviously you writing the author, rather than an imitation of the author that could not be told apart from one of their actual pieces.

Are you unenthused about the work? Enthusiasm is a major impetus in this kind of story, and you'll find it hard to work on a piece that you're not happy about working on. If you can, I'd put it aside; if you can't, then you need to figure out how to build enthusiasm, whether it's finding the fun bits to start with, playing writing games designed to expand your understanding of the piece you're working on, or even reading deeper in the source material in order to connect better with it.

Next steps

You do need to read plenty of whoever you're stealing from, and yet avoid letting their style possess you utterly. I would urge you to read a few works multiple times rather than trying to read everything they've done. Once you've read through a piece, perform those successive readings with an eye towards figuring out what it is the writer is doing and how they achieve the effects that they manage to reach.

There are some people who almost all of us have stolen from, at one time or another. Austen, Chaucer, Homer, and Shakespeare are but a few. Find interesting case studies in what other people have done, particularly where you may think that they have gone wrong.

How does the story that you're stealing work—and what's its emotional core (which doesn't have to be the same one that your story ends up with)? Summarize it in two or three sentences.

Exercises

1. Write a few paragraphs that are an imitation of the piece, one that a savvy reader would have difficulty telling from the original. OA: do an entire scene.
2. Try to find a distinctive voice in fiction and write a continuation of one of their stories. OA: do this multiple times.
3. Find a story you have always loved and create your own version of it.

Case study: (A Querulous Flute of Bone)

A number of years ago, I was invited to participate in a shared world project, the Fathomless Abyss, and as part of that, asked to write a story for the anthology that would launch the book, Tales from the Fathomless Abyss.

When I sat down to write the story, I had a lot of difficulty. in the end, I decided to borrow from a story I'd recently read and loved, O. Henry's "The Pimiento Pancakes," a love story set on the Western frontier.

First I had to decide what I was taking, which was basically the plot synopsis: a love triangle and how it is resolved. I wanted to change things up, so I mapped the love triangle against a race, the Geniod, that changed its gender at will. Rather than make the object that the antagonist is supposedly chasing a recipe, I made it something else, and in the process came up with the philosopher-king Nackle and his theory of objects.

I think this is one of the best stories I've written so far.

A Querulous Flute of Bone

There are, wherever wealth has accumulated enough to create the idle, those who collect things. Such collections may vary from those who catalog every cast off bit of flesh or chitin they shed to those who look outside themselves for art, or titillation, or an oblivion in which they might forget everyday life. They may consist the most mundane objects: string, or chewed up paper, or broken teacups, for example – or take on outré forms: dioramas made of nihlex bone (death to be found with in certain areas), or squares of cloth exposed to the Smog, prized for the oracular patterns of dirt left deposited on the fabric, or the tiny snowflakes of metal that are said to have fallen into the world during an Opening over a century ago.

Ector was such a collector. S/he was one of the Geniod, whose gender varies according to mood, and location, and other private considerations, and who are known, in the face of great trauma, to forget who they are and become entirely different personalities, their old selves never to be resumed or spoken of. Some races adulate them for this, others mock them, and such excess has driven the Geniod to be a race that keeps to itself, not by law, but preference.

Ector was an oddity in its own preferences, for it was willing to travel, to go farther than the rest of its race, driven by the desire to augment its collection, choosing to focus only on its quest.

The items it sought, ranging up and down the Tube in expeditions funded by two sets of indulgent grandparents and a much less indulgent set of parents, were things that could be considered metaphors for the world and the state of those in it. In this pursuit, it followed the strictures of the philosopher-king Nackle, who described the emotions that such objects evoked in the beholder in one five hundred page monograph and the intellectual effect of such exposure in a second, even longer volume.

Ector had studied at the knee of an ancient Human who had himself been instructed by Nackle, and the teaching had impressed it with a gravity and depth of the sort that scores the soul and directs all its movements in later years. Its search was a tribute to Nackle's ideas, for it looked for the things that Nackle posited existed, which could only be discovered by matching the emotion they evoked with that described in Nackle's pages, a task that required the laborious memorization of all of the philosopher's works.

Nackle's theory, insofar as such a thing can be simplified, was this: twenty one types of emotion exist in the world. Certain artifacts create emotions in the viewer, emotions unaffected by the viewer's history or idiosyncrasies of personality, but which are basic to the existence of all intelligent creatures. There are literally hundreds of sub-emotions, ranging from a soul's regret when it wishes to sing but cannot, to the joy of carrying on one's ancestral line in the face of tremendous adversity. To find the artifacts that replicated the base emotion, the one from which all the smaller sub-emotions sprang, one must move through a progression of refinement of the senses, created by the search for and exposure to artifacts exemplifying the emotions Nackle described.

This simplification would be objected to by most of Nackle's followers, who would point to subtleties of one kind or another, but truth be told, the theory was relatively uncomplicated, and it was the lengthy cataloging of emotions that gave the philosophy density rather than any complex thought.

As such, it was relatively easy to follow and Ector intended to devote its life to the process. It demanded a certain purity of thought, a willingness not to mire oneself in the petty details of life that Ector was more than happy to embrace, even though at times it felt a little lonely in the superiority of its perceptions. It eschewed most pleasures, and had never moved beyond the simplest gender, the one that everyone has, and had never thought of itself as he or she.

As is often the way in this world (or any other), Ector had a rival in its ambitions, Corint, another Geniod who had studied at the same philosopher's knee and delighted in challenging all of Ector's words in class, to the point where it sometimes feared to speak and would keep silent until the other's glee in pronouncements, often wrong, moved it to contradict what Corint said. The rivalry was bitter as tomb-wine, as bright as the sunstrip at its most fervid mid-day heat.

They thwarted each other whenever they could, until the action became second nature, unquestionable. Ector would search for the horn that had inspired melancholy for traditions that had faded into the past, only to find Corint there first, tucking it away in its pouch with a smile as greasy as the black oil that seeps near the rocks on which the iron and gears of the city of Indrus are perched. Or Corint would arrive at the Watershed shop rumored to hold the kaleidoscopic marble of joy in complexity of color and see Ector standing in the doorway, balancing it in his palm, watching hues roil in its depths.

They had chased each other downward this time, a journey through nest villages and bridge towns and basket farms. While in a cavern city's tavern chamber, Ector had overheard a scrap of conversation indicating it might have stumbled across a trail that would lead to an artifact falling in a category that had previously proved frustrating with its elusiveness: appreciation. This artifact might, Ector thought, actually lead its perception to spring along the ladder more than a few rungs; it was supposed to induce the appreciation of something's innate qualities. Rumor held that those capable of mastering it became able to make wonderful things: paper masks that spoke, stews that made the eater capable of dancing all day and night, or clothing that masked a wearer's every defect until they were so noble and upright in appearance that populaces flocked to elect them mayor or ruler or demagogue or whatever form of leadership they practiced.

Paradoxically, the trail led Ector upward and back to a Genoid village, Halah, that it had not visited since a child so small that it had barely learned to walk on its own feet. The village was famed for its hot springs, and the baths that had been carved out of the rock in order to allow visitors to take the waters, some of which smelled of sulfur, others of copper, and others of harder to identify minerals. All that Ector remembered of the place was the scented moisture of the air, and the trouble that its occupants had to take to scrub the black mold off their doorsteps and walls and other surfaces, lest it grow so shaggy and furry that it overran the place until it became one of the ghost towns that sometimes can be found along the Tube, places where one problem or another has ousted the inhabitants: plague or parasites or over-eager bandits.

It left in the time before dawn, trusting that Corint would still be sleeping and that when it woke, the rival would interrogate the innkeeper and be given the false story that Ector had planted, that Ector had taken the basket lift downward, headed to the savage tunnel jungle that was said to lurk only a few leagues on. It laughed to think of Corint, bewildered, searching in vain among fruitless dangers. It did not wish the other dead, but disaccomodated, perhaps even to a physical extent, was not unwelcome.

Then Ector thought that perhaps such vengeful contemplation was unworthy, would act to derange the perceptions, making them incapable of appreciating nuance. As it walked, taking the long spiraling trail to wound upward to the next settlement, it sorted through the objects that it carried about its person, the heart of its collection, twenty one objects, each representing advancement along a separate line of comprehension, towards perfect knowledge of the original emotion, and took each out in turn and looked at it, refreshing its knowledge of the object's essence and helping sway its soul away from any possible sullying of its evolving nature.

***

When he arrived at Halah, which was located inside a series of caverns, each with its own set of springs and a clever alignment of mirrors reflecting light from the sunstrip into its depths, the village smelled just as he remembered, a wet smell that crept inside the lungs and lingered there, moistly caressing the tissues until they burned. It was night so he took a room at an inn in the first cavern, thinking that he would go and look in the neighborhood where the artifact had been secreted, according to the conversation he'd overheard. It occurred to him, a brief paranoid thought, that perhaps Corint had planted the conversation to divert its rival away from something else.

The inn, which took advantage of the direct light seeping in through the entrance, was built of stone, and unlike most, had several stories, due to the permissive height of the cavern. When Ector roused in the morning, he could hear, from his room on the third floor, the sounds of the village and the inn, the sort of sounds that are pleasant when you're lingering in bed, conscious that you have no deadline. He drowsed and planned his day. The search would begin immediately after breakfast. He wondered what the object would look like, for all he had to go by was the description of the emotions it evoked.

He was coming down the stairs when he saw her.

He stopped, dead still, on the third step, to the dismay of the servant following him, a Genoid with a load of linens in her arms, for she collided with him with a whoof, the force throwing the fabric up into the air until for a moment Ector was suspended as though in white clouds, able only to see the thing that had caught its attention.

It is of little use to describe what distinguishes a Geniod's sense of beauty when it comes to their own species: a certain evenness of features, a nose that slanted rather than curved, a particular curl to a fanged eyetooth (check).

Suffice it to say that she was beautiful to Ector, and he could feel changes deep in his body as he responded to her.

Ignoring the sputtering of the servant as she gathered up the cloth, he stared.

On her part, she took no notice, though it was unclear whether this was due to obliviousness or disdain, vanishing through a doorway that he thought might lead to the kitchen.

Once she had gone through that door, it was as though the spell that had imprisoned him, allowing him only to look and breath and hear the hammering of his heart, had been broken and he could move again. He knelt to help the maid with the last of the linens, but she only glowered, and did not thank him for it.

He took a Kihlain coin from his pocket and held it up, letting its light waver over her features, which smoothed into a mask as she eyed its promise and waited for him to speak.

"The person who just went through that door," he said, pointing. "Who is she?"

"That be the child of this household," the maid said. "The only heir and well-loved, When you eat here, you be eating the food that comes from her pots. She's famous for it." She puffed a little with pride but said nothing more, eyes fixed on the coin in his hand.

He spun it in his fingers, let it roll over his knuckles and dance back into his hand. He felt the weight of the moment on his shoulders; slowly it squeezed the words out of him, "And her name?"

"Trice," the maid said, and snatched the coin before it fell, because the syllables echoed in his ears like singing bells until he could think of nothing else.

***

He did not go search for his artifact that day. Instead he lingered over his meal, trying to find traces of her in the excellent soup, the limpid beer, the sausages as fat and feisty as fighting pups. Sometimes she came out, bringing a dish to the sideboard, and he tried to be the first to reach it, to lay his fingers where hers had touched, as though he could absorb knowledge of her through his skin.

Finally they cleared away, and he kept sitting there in the common room, waiting. After near to an hour, she emerged, her apron put aside, and a basket on her arm.

Springing to his feet, he approached, asking if she were going forth to harvest fungi. When she nodded, he introduced himself and volunteered to carry her basket.

For a moment, he thought she would refuse him, and the shy blush that rode her cheeks only made her all the more entrancing to him, for it is a known thing that the entity which proves elusive is ever more alluring than that which comes readily to the hand. But in the end, she assented, and he followed at her heels, the basket in his hand.

Little conversation passed between them, and when he asked her questions, her answers were short and brief of detail. But he didn't mind, because every sound from her mouth made him tingle from his mouth to his toes.

When they returned, he was horrified to see Corint at the common fire, giving him a sardonic look as it noted his newly-donned masculinity. But he comforted himself with the thought that his rival would go after the artifact, rather than this new treasure that Ector had found. In fact, he decided, he would give the rival all the information he had, and let Corint have the joy of its discovery.

He took care, though, to give Trice the coldest of nods. There was no sense in giving Corint any clue what was happening.

When he went upstairs, he took his pack out from under the bed and spread out its contents. He took up his most recent acquisition, a querulous flute of bone, its origin unknown, its surface spiderwebbed with fine cracks. Nackle said that one of the main emotions was fear, but that all fears came from a particular type, the fear of the world lest it hurt one. Ector put his lips to the mouthpiece and blew, so softly that it was less than a baby's first breath. The sound that emerged was sad and scared and resolute, but he could not narrow it down, because it was fear, he was sure of that, but the nuances in it were unfamiliar to him.

It occurred to him that if he fell in love, he would no doubt blunt his perceptions, undo all the careful work that he had undertaken to fine-tune his consciousness and make him the fine artifact hunter he had become. But it didn't matter. He had a new purpose now.

He would write to his parents, tell them he had decided to settle in Halah. He would study to become a merchant, for what better way could there be to employ all the knowledge he had gathered in his wide-ranging quest? He was better traveled than the vast majority of his race, and he might as well use the fruits of that travel to earn a living that would make him a desirable partner. His parents would be bewildered but pleased; his grandparents less so of either, but equally ready to send him tokens of affectionate well-wishes in his new home: a blanket of knotted mushroom fiber and ceramic jars of fermented pickled cabbage.

He listened to the sounds of the inn all around. Someone in the room below him was walking back and forth, an impatient, thinking pace, and Ector wondered what might concern them. Downstairs was the noise of revelry and the beginnings of the dinner smells, little wafts of scent that crept under his door curtain to speak to him of cinnamon and sage and browned butter with fragments of garlic sizzling in it.

He could scarcely wait for dinner, but he bided his time, went down only when he heard other footsteps descending.

The food was unimaginably good. Roots broke open to send up steam, their insides flecked with pepper, and a tangy, pickley sauce overlaid the fresh greens. The meat was unfamiliar, but another diner said it was a bird newly come to this level, migrated from somewhere down below.

"They say it means an Opening is coming soon," Ector's fellow diner said, nodding wisely. "There are always signs and portents."

Ector forked another bite of meat and ate it. It was delicious, soaked in a sauce unexpectedly sweet and savory all in the same mouthful. The savor thrilled through him, and he closed his eyes, trying to pick out every nuance of the spices.

When he opened them, he saw Corint and Trice together, talking.

Fear clamped his legs and arms, a sense of panic that ran through him like electricity, made him as unable to move as an abandoned puppet. And even as he stared across the room, helpless, Corint's eyes met his and his rival smiled, letting Ector see his own newly-chosen gender, rivals even in this.

***

He did not want to talk to him, but he had to. Surely Corint could be warned off, or appealed to, or bought off? Trice was not an artifact, after all.

But, as it turned out, Corint had other suspicions regarding her and artifacts.

"The food's the clue," he said to Ector over too much wine, hearty swallows of it following slivers of cheese. "Is that how you found her too?"

Ector had learned, long ago, that silence often elicited more information than you thought it would. To other people, it often implied that you knew much much more than you were saying, and this proved the case with Corint. "Of course it was," he said before Ector could fill in anything else. "How could anyone produce such food unless they had learned to appreciate the ingredients, to gather them together in a jigsaw of tastes that fit so smoothly together that you cannot tell where one leaves off and the next begins?" He sighed, and his breath rippled across the surface of the carved stone cup in front of him. "Imagine that such a pretty young woman could hold the key to such a thing! She must have found it somewhere. Oh course I became male, it's clearly the best way to gain her trust."

Relief washed through Ector. Corint wanted the artifact he thought Trice must have, not Trice herself and now that Ector considered it, of course that would be why the food at the inn was so extraordinary. In contemplating the artifact, Trice must have absorbed its lesson well, in order to create such dishes.

Despite all their past difficulties, the happiness that surged through him at this realization made him regard Corint, good old Corint, always reliable, always there, differently. He decided that honesty would be the best policy. He would be a new, changed being now, one who spoke the truth in a way worthy of the woman he adored.

"I will help you find the artifact," he said earnestly. "All I want is Trice." He felt a little pang at the thought of an artifact in Corint's hands, he couldn't help that, it was old habit, but he pushed it aside. What he was seeking was much better.

Corint regarded him with a trace of suspicion that faded at the sincerity evident in Ector's face.

"Very well," he said. "Help me with that, and I will help you in turn."

***

True to his word, Ector broached the word of the artifact the next day while he and Trice were gathering pallid watercress from the river that spilled into the Tube near the entrance to the village. He did so delicately. He didn't want her to think that he attributed her skill at cookery with some force outside herself; he must let her know that he acknowledged it as part of herself, intrinsic. And therefore, he thought, now that she had cultivated the sensibility that allowed her to cook so through no-doubt unconscious contemplation of the artifact (for she had avowed no knowledge whatsoever of Nackle when Ector had broached the topic the day before.)

But when he edged towards the subject, she skittered away, sought refuge in all manner of topics: the mating habits of crawdads, the sounds of dying unicorns, the secret name of the Nihilex Queen and whether that entity remained the same person from year to year.

At length he gave up; she seemed relieved.

***

That night in his room, listening to the sounds of the village through the open window of his room, hearing distant snores and stony echoes, he thought about less than a week ago, when all his heart had been given to artifact hunting.

Those days seemed as distant as though they had fallen down the Tube like an addled suicide, leaving only their confused and water-colored ghosts behind. He remembered the fever of finding an object that completed a series, the glossy joy that could color days on end, at least until the itch for some other part of the chain drove him elsewhere. Should he give what he had collected already, what he carried with him, to Corint? His fellow was one of the few who could appreciate the nuances of some of the objects; to do anything else was to waste them, surely, and if he kept his collection, wouldn't it just nag at him to go back to it, like the wine kept for sickness and cooking eats at an alcoholic through mere knowledge of its location.

He would wait. He would see.

He played his flute long into the night.

***

As the days wore on, he began to think Trice was some sort of Guardian; whatever artifact inspired her cooking also her hereditary charge. Such things were not unknown; many of the artifacts that Nackle described had guardians of one kind or another.

If this were the case, to get the object and persuade his rival away, he must ask her to betray her order. He agonized over the ethics of the situation – what would Nackle have done, under what emotion would this worry have been placed, and what sort of artifact could possibly evoke it, other than the living one that was Trice, built of sinew and bone, of blood and hair and hands and eyes?

She knew he was wooing her, she acknowledged it, and let him speak of love and what he had to offer. But let the slightest syllable close to artifact cross his lips and she was on to other subjects, grown cold and distant one time, flurried and a mass of distraction the next.

He put on weight, eating deep of her dishes every morning, every evening. His pants were tight, and he discarded his belt entirely, then went to the tailor and ordered two new sets of clothes for everyday. He studied at the merchant's guild, working towards his license, and continued to stay at the village inn, despite the lack of economy the choice represented, since he could have (and was offered the chance to, more than once) rented a room in someone's house.

Corint also confessed himself unable to elicit any information from Trice about the artifact that allowed her to cook so well, despite his many conversations with her and his offers to assist her in the kitchen during the day, peeling roots, washing greens, and engaging in a myriad more chores that were, he told Ector, designed to find a chance to snoop and discover where Trice had hidden the artifact.

It seemed to Ector that as time wore on, the girl's parents regarded him with a certain sympathy. Sometimes they waved aside the payment for an evening meal, saying it was on the house since he was such a faithful customer. It unnerved him, the look in their eyes, it made all will ooze from his veins.

He tried to stop playing the flute at night, but it soothed him. It let him sleep. Unless he played it, he found himself waking throughout the night, every time there was a footfall or a distant conversation. The inn was in the cavern closest to the Tube and sometimes he could even hear the wind rushing there, a sound almost as sad and lonely as the flute's.

***

This had gone on for three weeks when he ran, by chance, into another artifact hunter, one who had not studied with the same tutor as Corint and Ector, thereby enabling an ease of interchange not always possible among fellow students. This was a human hunter, who lacked in senses but possessed the ability to make great leaps of logic. Indeed, after inviting him to a meal, she divined the circumstances in the space of time between appetizer and entrée and got him to admit to them in a series of pointed questions.

Her look, when the interrogation was over, was pitying in a way that reminded him of Trice's parents. The feeling sharpened when she tactfully steered away from discussion of his old obsession, as though it were a former lover whose new relationship might have saddened or infuriated him. The look was on his mind when he returned to the inn, determined to have it out once and for all with Trice. He would lay his heart bare, would explain all that he was thinking and feeling and hoping and perhaps in return she would embrace him or perhaps she would spurn him, but either would be better than this aimless existence, this void of not knowing what to do or say in order to gain what he so desperately wanted.

At the inn, Trice's parent stood feeding the little bats in the courtyard. The creatures flittered back and forth in unsteady flight, snatching morsels from their fingertips. The air was full of their squeaks, just on the edge of hearing, audible enough to be annoying and yet still out of range.

Ector said, as he approached, "Is Trice in the kitchen? I must speak to her."

The parent blinked. "She's gone to be married," they said.

Ector gaped. "Married? To whom?"

"That fellow Corint."

Ector stood in silence for a moment, his lips parted but not breathing. His face twitched, just below the left eye, a persistent, maddened twitch of nerves pushed past their limit.

At length, he said, "Well. I suppose that's one way to gain her artifact."

The parent set the pan of grubs down and clasped him on the shoulder. "Ah, lad," they said. "Corint told us of your odd obsession."

"My odd obsession?" Ector said, not moving, his tone as bland as unsullied paper.

"These artifacts, the ones you seized on due to brain fever and too much studying. You must realize they are imaginary, my good fellow. Corint explained it all to us."

"Then Trice had no artifact," Ector said.

The parent gawped at him in turn. "Why would you believe such a thing?"

"Her food."

"You thought her cooking was due to some magical object?" The parent laughed, and somewhere inside there was an echo from the common room as someone there made their own joke. "Lad, she's been cooking since she was able to lift a wooden spoon, and cooking not just for her family, but for an innsworth of critics every time. It is a more demanding school for a cook than any academy."

"Corint told Trice of my...odd obsession as well?"

"Ay, and she was hard pressed to keep you from the topic sometimes, she said. But she knew that if you were allowed to talk at length about them, you would fall prey to one of the fits that Corint described. Trice is a tender soul; she did not want to see you fall prey to such circumstances."

Ector stood for a while longer as though absorbing all of these things a morsel at a time, letting the meaning seep into him until he could comprehend it. His face gave nothing away, shuttered as a cliff-face window.

***

In later years he went back to artifact hunting, although never with the same relish that he had once exhibited. He did not travel as far as he once had, and he never returned to the village where Beatrice and Corinth lived.

He carried with him a packful of his artifacts. On the day that he had learned of Beatrice's marriage, he had returned to his room and smashed the querulous flute of bone. But then he reconstructed it, albeit in a different shape.

It was a heart-shaped thing now, with hollow tubes running through it until it was empty and as light as though it was a thought and not an actual object. Prone to turn in the hand, slicing bone-deep if you were not careful how you touched it. Sometimes he held it, because it evoked a set of emotions as deep and true as any he had ever experienced, a set that Nackle had described in the category of loss, which outweighed any fear of hurt. Indeed, that fear seemed as unimportant as the scars on his hands where the artifact had bitten time and time again, writing its own addendum to Nackle's final text.

CHAPTER 5
CULTURALLY DETERMINED STRUCTURE

What it is

This is a structure that has a particular kind of cultural weight to it, and you want to be careful in these waters, because sometimes they get a little deep and perilous. You want to be respectful of cultures that are outside the mainstream, and I'm defining the mainstream as the people that television broadcasts are predominantly aimed at: white, affluent, heterosexual, and able-bodied, to name a few. This mainstream has odd and ill-defined edges but most people can identify it.

I earlier said that great artists steal, and that statement still works, I think. But you must be aware that if your culture and the culture that you are stealing from are markedly different, it will be extremely difficult for you to make it your own without people eying you askance and questioning what you have done. And that is a reasonable question, in my opinion.

One of the best resources I can recommend for this sort of discussion is *Writing the Other*, by Nisi Shawl and Cynthia Ward. It talks about the idea of blinders, of things that are so built into your own cultures (because we all exist in multiple ones) that you have trouble perceiving them when writing in a different culture. You literally cannot perceive these hindrances to your vision until you manage to get outside them somehow.

What it provides

As with other forms, you are given a useful set of conventions, premade templates that you will fill with your words. The words that you fill them with are what makes the story, and in order for it to be your story those words must reflect you. At the same time, you owe it to the culture that has created the structure to treat it with the respect its history deserves.

Considerations

Why are you choosing to use this form rather than others? What is it about this form that calls to you? What made you start reading it in the first place and where is the point that the story occurred to you?

What do you want to celebrate—and/or change—about the form? What parts of it must you keep in order for it to feel satisfying?

What are you trying to accomplish with the form? What sorts of emotional hearts does this form usually have, and can you subvert it while remaining respectful of the original material?

Pitfalls

You don't know enough about the form and the context in which it has emerged. You find yourself at a loss. This is usually easily remedied through two of the possible next steps, reading deeply in the form and reading what people have said about the form. For example, if it's a sonnet, find out what definitions of sonnet people have used. Look for famous examples of sonnets. Read about the history of the form and the first examples of it.

You are picking the form for reasons that have nothing to do with the story. Perhaps you simply want to experiment, or perhaps you are thinking of it in some other terms, such as marketing, or writing in a space that other people are not. I'm hesitant to say that a particular motivation for writing a story is wrong, but I do think that sometimes sincerity—and its converse—in motivation comes across in writing, whether or not the writer is trying to do so.

Next steps

Figure out what defines success. What do you like about the form, what would make you feel you had done a good job in creating one?

Read deeply in the form. Find examples all over the chronological spectrum if possible, both ancient examples and modern day ones.

Read what people have said about the form. There is plenty of literary criticism out there, much of it available on the Internet. You don't need to agree with everything or take what other people say as an absolute truth, but time spent investigating what other people have said will richen your response and make it more informed. You may also run across additional pitfalls in your research.

Figuring out commonalities. What is symptomatic of the form, including all the meta-things about it, such as title, means of presentation, time period, etcetera?

Exercises

1. Come up with a list of possible forms (review, guide, menu, letter, encyclopedia article, game instructions). pick one and figure out a possible plot that would go with it. OA: do three possible plots.
2. Think of a written form that you associate with a particular emotion: a newspaper announcement about a wedding (usually happiness), an obituary (sadness), a tax bill (anxiety). Now write one that creates the opposite emotion; a sad wedding announcement, a happy obit, a complacent tax bill. OA: make it convey both emotions at once.

Case study: (Narrative of a Beast's Life)

"Narrative of a Beast's Life," which originally appeared in Realms of Fantasy, uses the structure of the slave narratives written in 18th and 19th centuries by enslaved Africans. They were accounts of the horrors endured by slaves, and they were an important factor in the Abolitionist movement in America.

I had read some of these in college, but before I began, I read more deeply, including what's considered the first example of such a narrative, *Interesting Narrative of the Life of Olaudah Equiano; or, Gustavus Vassa, the African, Written by Himself* (1789), which ended up providing some of my story's underlying plot, but also determined the shape: small chapters, each with its own heading describing the events contained.

Using this narrative structure worried me. My task was to celebrate the form and show something new about it while respecting its origins, which is more complicated than taking something and twisting it into a commercial form. It's my hope that people reading my story may look to the original narratives, or at least become aware of their existence.

I knew at this point that this was what the Tabat stories were about, the struggle of the Beasts to be free, and how their oppressors demonized and infantilized them. For another story that connects to this one, look to "Primaflora's Journey," in *Beneath Ceaseless Skies*, which tells you more of Phillip's eventual fate, or novels *Beasts of Tabat* or *Hearts of Tabat.*

Narrative of a Beast's Life

Part I

An account of my family and village – our circumstances – childhood pastimes – Bozni's fate – Adrato's lesson

Like many of my fellow Beasts, I was born to freedom, in a small village named Dekalion, the confluence of five centaur herds. The youngest of seven, I was a favorite of my family, not just of my parents and siblings, but of my aunts, uncles, and cousins as well. They named me Fino, which means "Quickwitted" in my milk tongue, and I grew up in an atmosphere of love and encouragement that any Human child might envy.

Since many have asked me of that initial society, I will set down what I remember of life there. Our village resided in the shade of sandstone cliffs, which overlooked plains of acacia trees and brambles. My people hunted, and the men had farms of cassava and gourds, corn and plantains.

The village was located three or four days inland from the sea, and only a scant number of our women went to trade on the coast or with other neighboring settlements. Only bold women, past their first childbearing and used to fighting, because slavers were common. The traders traveled in groups of five or six, armed with bows and spears, and took goods: bark cloth, carved water gourds, reed baskets. They brought back bright cottons and bits of metal, and sometimes dried fish, tasting of salt and smoke and unfamiliar spices.

When I was a child, my favorite playmate was Bozni, a clever boy perhaps a year younger than myself. We played together, along with our fellows, under the watchful eye of an elderly centaur, Adrato. In the hot afternoons, he was prone to falling asleep in the shade, and we would play where we liked while he drowsed.

The town was a series of huts, woven of thorn and branches, thatched with grass. In the morning, pairs of centaurs would take clay jugs to fill them in the mud-colored river that ran near the village.

This river was not a safe place, and we children were forbidden its shores, which naturally rendered them the most desirable of playgrounds in our eyes. We learned that dangling a branch over the deeper pools might bring a grim-jawed crocodile boiling out of the water.

While leaning out over a pool with a branch one day, Bozni was snatched by such a monster. The rest of the children screamed and ran for help, but I leaped forward, trying in vain to pull him from the reptile's maw. I took up the fallen branch and beat the creature about the head, Bozni shouting and screaming all the while.

Alas! Try as I might, the crocodile withdrew further into the water, where it spun itself sideways several times as quickly as a child's top. Bozni thrashed past in the foaming water – I believe he perished early in those moments, but the crocodile continued to shake the corpse.

I stood horrified, staring into the reddening river, and caught a last glimpse of his ensanguined face, barely visible against the water's rusty color. By the time Adrato came galloping up, summoned by the others, Bozni was gone.

Adrato demanded an account of what had transpired, and forbore his anger at my inability to express the horrific scene I had just witnessed. Bit by bit, he coaxed the tale from me.

At its conclusion, we stared at each other for a long moment. He took me by the shoulder and pointed a doleful finger at the river. By now, the current had washed away any stain from the glistening banks, although the dents and troughs dug in the mud by the frantic action of Bozni's legs bore testament to the struggle.

"That is the price of disobedience," Adrato said sternly, and shook me once or twice. His demeanor impressed me so gravely that it would not be until I was an adult that I fully realized that in some cases, the price of obedience might prove still more costly. I was free then, as I said, and a child. I did not understand many things, and so I swore I would always obey, lest I meet Bozni's fate.

Part II

My early education – anticipation of a hunt – a raid in the night by Shifters – my capture – our journey

We children were taught mathematics, which I took to with great delight and facility of mind. We learned nothing of the written word, but we were taught to calculate with cabi, which means "counting beads," carved of ivory and strung on cords.

The arts of hunting and self-defense were also taught us. When a centaur youth came of age, he or she would kill a lion in order to receive the tattoos of adulthood along their arms and chest. As the day for my hunt came nearer, dreams of what was to happen filled all my nights. I made two spears for the purpose and Adrato promised me an iron knife for the occasion.

But a week before the ritual was to take place, a slaving clan of Shifters – who sometimes walked in two-legged form, and other times ran as hyenas – attacked us. Our traders had left that morning, and our attackers must have been watching for that signal. In the darkest hours of the night, they set fire to several huts and shouted angrily beside the windows, thrusting spears inward at the sleepers, before withdrawing.

In the confusion, amid the noise and flames, I ran in the wrong direction, fetching up against a fence and knocking myself sharply on the head. I reeled away into the darkness outside the village walls and found myself seized by rough hands, which pulled sacking down over my head, obscuring my vision and securing my arms. I kicked out, but my captors quickly secured me and I found myself trussed and thrown on a cart with several others. We tried to ascertain each others' identities, but savage blows rained down on us with imprecations and commands for silence. The cart trundled into motion and we rumbled away.

The next few days we traveled in this manner. My companions in captivity were revealed as three other youths, ranging in age from myself, my age-mates Tsura and Kali, and an older boy named Flik. We tested our bonds, but our captors were evidently well-experienced at their brutal profession. They watered us and fed us with grain porridge, but so little that we were weakened by hunger and tormented by thirst, along with biting flies that crawled over us as we jostled along in the miserably hot sun.

Sometimes I tried to convince myself that my family would come for me, but at least a week would pass before our traders returned from their mission. They were the only ones brave enough to dare searching for us, but by the time they were set on our trail, it would be cold.

Part III

We are taken to market – I am sold to a new master – Our journey and its hardships – A garden feast – The Sphinx's name - We come to Samophar and are taken aboard ship

We were taken to a market in a city. None of us had ever seen such a place before and there were sights and sounds and smells such as I had never witnessed. The buildings were made of clay brick, laid together so snugly that no mortar or cement was necessary. Some buildings were built on top of each other, and stairs meant for no Centaur led up and down the outside.

Here we were sold, each to separate masters. Mine fastened me in a coffle with other beings: a Sphinx of that city that had committed murder, two Djinni, and a snake-headed woman. Oxen drew the cart to which we were shackled, and chained on it was a Dragon, not a large one, but some eight feet in length. A small herd of goats marched behind us in turn, intended for the Dragon's sustenance.

We traveled northward for three days, during which I picked up a scattering of my comrades' languages, and they of mine. The Dragon, as it chanced, spoke the Sphinx's tongue. As they talked back and forth, I listened and tried to make sense of what they said. I could not assemble the Dragon's words into meaning, but they drove the Sphinx to silent tears. She wept all day and well into the night, and did not speak again for days.

I had never seen a Sphinx before and when at last she could be coaxed into speech, I gave her my name and tried to learn her own. But my companions informed me that no Sphinx speaks their name outside their own kind. I was much amazed at this strange practice, for it was the first time I realized that it was not simply places that differed from those I had known, but customs as well.

The Djinni were kindly disposed towards me, saying that I reminded them of their own child, who had been sold away from them. They tried to give me a portion of their food, but I refused it, even though it tempted me sorely. They were as hungry as I, and I had no right to deprive them. I thought it unfair that one creature should eat while another starved, even then before I had seen how bitter injustice might be.

On the second day, we came across a village that lay in ashes. Its living inhabitants were all gone, but here and there in the blackened ruins were corpses: long-armed apes and centaurs like myself. Our master allowed us to forage in the gardens, although we were kept chained together, rendering walking laborious. While much was trampled, I found some yams there and put them in a sack I found to one side, along with stalks of sugar cane, two lemons, and a handful of orange fruit that I had never seen before, sized to match my thumb tip, thin-skinned, and full of a sour savor. We roasted our pickings in the guards' fire that night, and considered ourselves to be dining as well as royalty.

The next day we came to a seaport, which a passerby told us, in answer to our entreaties, was Samophar. Here the larger buildings were made of white stone and the streets underfoot were paved with yellow brick. Fatbellied ships rode at anchor in the harbor and we realized that our owner intended to sell us away from our homeland.

I had never seen so much water. I stared at it, imagining crocodiles beneath the glittering surface. At the docks, we were passed over to a ship's master. I witnessed other slaves being loaded onto the ship, and saw the weeping of several families being parted.

Here a sad incident came to pass. The two Djinni were chained together and contrived to jump into the waves. The woman drowned before they could be drawn up out of the water and the husband was savagely beaten by the sailors, angry at the trouble he had afforded. Try as I might, despite the blows aimed my way, I could not force my way up the gangplank at first, but the Djinni's blood, his cries, forced me, lest I push them to such lengths for I knew they would have no mercy.

Below decks I found myself amidst a throng of other captives, including Dog-men from the east, ghouls, several Griffins, a family of Harpies, Ogres, Unicorns, and individuals: a Catoblepas and a Rakshasa. Above decks, I could hear the roaring of the Dragon as it was chained into place and we set underway.

Part IV

The voyage – We are rebuked by the Sphinx - I am given a new name – The fate of a cyclops

Brutality was a common practice of the Human crew towards the cargo. They affected to despise the Beasts they conveyed, and yet they used us venially as they desired, particularly the Ogre women. Few of the crew did not undertake such practices, either with each other or with the miserable captives in their care.

We were given a measure of gruel and water each day, which our keepers were not careful to hand out. Some bullies among us made it their practice to take the provisions of those who were sick or otherwise unable to defend what was rightfully their own. After a few such incidents, though, the Sphinx spoke to us. Those who could understand her words rendered them into other tongues and then others translated them in turn so a constant subdued whisper spread outward from her throughout the cramped hold.

She discoursed most remarkably in her deep, grave voice. She said as thinking beings we owed each other civil treatment and that it was the duty of the strong to protect the weak from the worst of our common oppression. She looked at each face in turn with her great brown eyes and some faltered under that stare.

After that, the bullies seemed abashed. From then on we kept better order among ourselves, despite the taunts and jeers of the sailors, who were angered by behavior. It was as tough it were a reproach that their captives might act more civilized than they. But we knew that without such acts, we had nothing.

Not even our names were our own. During the journey we were given new names, chosen by the Captain from a book which he carried as he walked the levels below decks, trailed by two sailors, pointing and giving each the appellation by which they were to be known from then forward.

The sound he gave me seemed strange and unrepeatable. Phil-lip. But the sailor behind him paused and said the name aloud to me and made me repeat it back until he was satisfied and moved on to the next Beast. Phillip. Resentment blazed in my chest, for it was not my name, not the name by which my parents and beloved siblings had known me. Was that not part of who I was – my very innermost nature? My name. Phil-lip.

But I did not give voice to my objections, for I had seen the example made of a resistor. A monstrous Cyclops, who was incongruously soft-spoken to the point where one must strain their ears to hear him, proved quite adamant on the subject of his name, refusing the one given him – Jeremy – and was beaten till he "should acknowledge it", which rather proved to be the point where he fainted and pails of sea water thrown on his face failed to revive him. He died two days later.

As the days passed, the realization struck me that I was moving away from my home, and that even should I escape my servitude, I would yet find myself in a strange land, when I knew no one to help me. Despondent at the thought, I refused to eat and gradually sank into a deep melancholy. It was evident that the sailors cared not whether I lived or died, but the Captain, who had a financial investment in his piteous cargo, forced them to shift me up onto deck in the sunshine and wind. I was placed towards the aft of the ship, in a somewhat sheltered spot, with several other invalids also deemed to be in danger of being carried away by their maladies.

One of these we knew doomed. A tree spirit named Malva who faded with each mile stretching between herself and her tree. The Captain swore greatly upon discovering the nature of her malady, for the seller had deliberately not warned him. She was the sweetest of souls and it was painful to watch her skin grow dull where once it had been luminous The strands of her hair fell prey to the sea winds, which snatched them away day by day and bore them who knows where.

After a week and a half of this existence, Malva finally breathed her last. The captain lost no time disposing of the corpse overboard and I forbore to watch, lest I see the gray sharks that followed us quarreling and tearing over the body.

The ghouls pleaded to be allowed to dispose of the corpse, as they did each time some unfortunate passed away. The Captain said he did not like to cultivate their habits, and for the most part, they were denied fresh meat except for such occasions as they were able to hide someone's death below decks.

In doing so, they did not have to hide their activities so much from the sailors, who paid us as little attention as they could, as from their fellows, most of whom objected to the thought of being disposed of in such a gruesome wise, although those entirely resigned to their fate said they did not mind being eaten by the ghouls.

Once again, Providence stepped in. Prompted by a chance fondness for my form and face, another being intervened and saved me from following Malva's dreadful fate. The cook, Petro, was a fat man who had once worked in a racing stable. He confided in me that his great desire had been to be a jockey, and that when at the age of twelve, he had realized that his frame would outstrip a rider's dimensions, he had run away to sea in despair.

Only Petro's nursing me with what fresh fruit he had stored away kept me alive. He took me as his pet, and delighted in asking for stories about my village and the Beasts I had encountered in the course of my travels. He was fascinated with the equine part of my body and would groom and caress it, while avoiding that part which seemed Human to him.

I went so far as to offer him my real name, but he shook his head and insisted that I must think of myself as Phillip from now on, else I might expect to gather unnecessary punishment on myself.

He explained to me that the world was divided into Humans and Beast, and that the Gods had given Humans dominion over Beasts, which meant that such creatures could not own themselves, and only be the possession of Humans. He would have offered to buy me, he assured me, except that I was far outside his meager savings. He spoke of the highness of my price as a good thing, because it ensured that someone wealthy, who would be able to maintain me well, would be my purchaser.

The Dragon was kept at the verymost back of the ship, which was reckoned less imperiled by its flames. Most of the time its jaws were kept prisoned, but at dawn and dusk, they would release its mouth to feed it a goat from the dwindling herd and let it drink its fill of water. The diet did not suit its bowels, and by the end of the trip, the back of the ship was covered with its gelid feces, despite the sailors' best efforts to keep it scrubbed free of the substance, which burned bare skin exposed to it.

As we went north, the weather became more and more winter-like. We all found the cold and damp excruciating. Clothing and blankets were at a premium, and many traded favors or begged bits of clothing from the sailors. Petro gave me his second-best jacket, which he said he had grown too paunchy for. It hung loose on me, but I was glad of the overabundance of the fabric.

We did not sit out on the deck any more, and so I did not witness our approach to the port of Tabat. Waiting in the darkness, I strained my ears to make out what I could: the cries of gulls, echoed by the shouts of Humans, the creak of the ship's timbers and the swish of water, the slap of waves.

When I left the ship, Petros had tears in his eyes as he waved to me, but I did not think much of him. All my worries were engaged by what was to come. Under the watchful eye of the Captain, we made our way down the gangplank that led from the ship to the dock, shivering in the bitter sea wind, uncertain of our fate.

Part V

We arrive in Tabat – the fate of the Dragon - I am sold – my new mistress – I am taken to Piper Hill

We were driven to a vast marketplace, a single roof stretched across hundreds of feet, and six raised platforms where the Beasts and each platform's Human auctioneer stood. Inside the walls, among the press of the crowd, it was much warmer, so warm that I felt in danger of fainting. The crowd pressed on every side, and the smells were oppressive.

I saw the Sphinx and others of my fellow captives sold. Then came the Dragon, which they hauled up onto the block in chains. The great iron muzzle was clamped around its jaws so it still could not speak, but it rolled its eyes in fury and tried to flap its wings.

Alas! It had been denuded of those members, and only stumps remained, treated with cautery and tar bandages. At the time

I wondered at the savagery of such a gesture and later learned it is customary with such Beasts with the power of flight, lest they come loose, since in such cases they invariably fly away as quickly as they can.

The bidding for the Dragon came fast and furious. At length it was sold and dragged away. The bidding was shorter in my case, and after a quick interchange, I was shoved in line behind my purchaser.

She was a lean woman with dark hair worn in an ornate braid wrapped around her head. Her skin was darker than my own and she was significantly shorter. She gestured at me to follow her, flanked by her guard, a shaggy-headed Minotaur who eyed me wordlessly. His arms were as big around as my chest, or so it seemed to me.

She bought another Beast, a dog-man. He and I walked in new sets of chains behind a cart heaped with produce and other goods bought in turn. I did not speak his language, nor he mine, and so we did not communicate much as we progressed along. At noon, we stopped to rest, and the woman and Minotaur ate lunch, although only drinks from a water skin were given to the dog-man and I.

We arrived at our destination by early evening. A series of whitewashed buildings sat atop a cliffside overlooking a small river. The houses seemed quite grand to me at the time, but after I had lived there for some time, I came to see that it was older, and had not been well tended. The bushes in the once lavish garden were overgrown, and in places the faster-growing ones had choked back the shyer, less-assuming plants. The garden grew all manner of medicinal herbs – some out right, others hidden between tree roots or in the shadows of the crumbling rock wall. The outer walls were shaggy with peeling paint, and the gutters drooped as though unable to bear the slightest thought of rain. This was Piper Hill, my new home, which it has remained until now.

Part VI

Jolietta begins my training – I am broken to harness – Brutus and Caesar – the dwarf dragons - I am sent out to work – I fall ill – I speak my feelings and am punished

I soon grew settled into life at Piper Hill. I set about learning the language as quickly as I could, stung by both Jolietta's scorn and her lash when she did not think I was applying myself as hard as I could. Jolietta showed me how to work in tandem with another centaur that she had in her stables, named Michael.

You would think that an intelligent creature would have little trouble with the concept of the harness, but the truth is that it required strength and dexterity that had not been developed in me by all my confined days aboard the slave ship.

My physical dexterity was also hampered by my injuries. The day after we arrived at the estate, Jolietta had me tied and whipped until the blood flowed. She told me that we should begin as we meant to go on – that to disobey her would be to get whipped again.

She demanded to know if I understood her. By now I could make out what she said, for it was the same language many of the sailors had spoken. She went on to tell me my name would continue to be Phillip, as that was the name written on my papers of ownership, but that if I dissatisfied her, she was quite capable of changing my name to something much more degrading.

By way of example, she was in the process of training an oracular pig, and she called that unfortunate being "Thing" and insisted that we all do the same, although the information quickly passed among us that the pig's birth name was Tirza.

I watched Tirza's training in tandem with my own, and found her sullen example a warning sign of my fate should I rebel too overtly. Like most of her kind, Tirza could speak aloud, as though she were human, a clear soprano which I had the pleasure of hearing sing on several occasions. She was a good enough soul when one spoke to her outside of Jolietta's training, but few of us dared hold such conversations, for fear of the beatings that we would be given if we were caught offering the miserable creature solace, either spoken or material.

I respected the two minotaur guards that Jolietta had with her almost constantly as she went about the estate on her daily business:

Brutus and Cassius. It had been Cassius that had gone with her on her buying trip. Neither of them deigned to speak to the other household Beasts, other than to pass along their mistress's orders or reprimand us if we mis-served them in some way. They had been with Jolietta, I was told, since they were still calves.

Other members of the household were an orangutan, two dryads belonging to nearby trees, a Satyr, two Dog-men who worked in the stable, an old Troll who served as cook, and Bebe, a fat old Centaur mare who oversaw the household and was greatly trusted by Jolietta. She was a sly creature, and I quickly learned to confide nothing in her, for she was fond of earning treats and favors from Jolietta by paying with small betrayals – or sometimes much larger – of the other servants.

The satyr, Hedonus, professed himself content in his role. He said when he had first been captured and sold, he had worked in the Southern Isles in a salt-making establishment. The Isles were not conducive to health. Hedonus said each year one out of every ten slaves died, and that this health rate, which was better than most, was reckoned to be due to a mixture of lime juice and sulfur that the overseer forced his workers to drink each morning. By contrast to the salt pond, Jolietta's establishment was luxury indeed, he inferred in conversation, more than once, and Bebe seemed to feel the same.

There were others who might not have agreed. Workers served on the estate and a larger group was hired out as needed. These groups were somewhat fluid – servants out of favor might find themselves hired out and conversely a hired worker who did well might find themselves purchased as part of the household or estate workers. While the household servants lived within the house itself and ate in its kitchen, the others lived in small cabins erected at the back of the estate.

Although the household accommodations were severe, they were luxurious by contrast with these cabins, which were caulked ineffectually with mud and cloth against the severities of the wind. I have stood in one during a storm and heard the whole cabin singing, as though it were nothing but a musical instrument for the wind to sound as it would.

Mistress Jolietta also raised what are called dwarf dragons, though they are not properly Dragons. They are used for sport hunting by the wealthy in that area, and a pack of them can bring down any creature known, for by themselves, one can capture a creature ten times its size, which can reach up to fifteen feet. These she set me to feeding each day, which meant that I must butcher two goats and several dozen chickens every morning. Tender-hearted, I wept whenever I killed the goats until Jolietta caught me at it and beat me for my tears. After that, I steeled my heart and killed each animal as though it were nothing more than wood set animate and bleating.

The dragons, of which there were a half dozen or so, were kept in a great pen set against the cliff face that also functioned as the rubbish heaps for the estate, for the dragons preferred to nest in such, and let the baking heat combined with the sun brood the eggs. The trees had been cut back so the sunlight could fully enter the pen, and it was a malodorous and noisome place where few cared to go. I took advantage of this to seek solitude in which to heal my injured spirit. I would sit thinking and listening to the rasp of the lizards' lovemaking – a sandpaper scrape that never seemed to cease, even when eggs were being laid in the pits scraped atop each heap of trash and nightsoil.

The dragons were worth a deal of money, I gathered. There were two clutches ready to hatch, and Jolietta set me to watching over them at night, sitting up with a torch, waiting to see any motion on a mother dragon's part that would betoken a hatching taking place.

The second day of the watch, I was so tired that I fell asleep and woke only when I heard the croaking from a female dragon that announced her progeny.

The tiny animals crawled out under their mother's watchful eye and headed for the shelter of the bale of straw Jolietta had directed me to put within a few paces of the heap.

One crawled beneath me, and I raised my foot, thinking to crush it and thus deprive my owner of a fine sum of money. But it was such a pretty little thing, only a foot long, with fine mottled patterns, distinct and new, along its scaly sides, and so I stayed my hoof and let it crawl into the straw. Dwarf dragons are as unthinking as animals, so I did not speak to it, now or then.

Those eggs hatched fine, but the other batch did not, and when this became evident due to the length of time that had passed, Jolietta held me accountable and beat me. While she had me beneath the lash, I cried out, saying that she had no right to do such a thing to me, and that I would run away, as soon as I was able.

She merely laughed at me and told me that in this land, there was no place that I could escape and live freely, and that I was much safer with her than I would be with some slave catcher ready to sell me elsewhere. Every hand would be against a runaway Beast, and I should be captured quite quickly and brought back for further punishment.

It would not be the last time she beat me, or that I saw another servant beaten. A small hut crouched towards the back of the estate, a great hook set dangling from its blackened roof beams. She would suspend the unfortunate victim by the wrists from this hook and the rest of the household be assembled in order to watch and learn from their unfortunate fellow's example.

Under Jolietta's tutelage, I learned the difference between the various methods of punishment: the searing flay of cat-tails, the bitter blow of a cow-hide whip, the thud of a rod against scarred flesh. Like other Humans I had met, she felt that the sooner examples were made, and the sooner a captive resigned to its life of servitude and toil, the better for all parties concerned.

Food was a constant worry among the Beasts of the household, although we did not live half so badly as the Beasts who were hired out to work on surrounding farms. They were given two pecks of corn and a pound of dried fish each week, and counted themselves better off than most. Nonetheless, they tried their best to be hired by the masters known for feeding their workers well, and the household Beasts smuggled out what they could of food. Most of the time, though, we ate the same mash and boiled vegetables that the Humans in the household, mainly Jolietta and her apprentices, consumed.

On the western edge of the estate there was a stand of apple trees. Jolietta allowed us to pick these as we would, for she disliked the taste of the fruit, and would watch one of us gobble a piece down, amazement evident on her face as she made loud remarks regarding how she did not understand how we might stomach such noisome provender. Despite this talk, we ate the apples with relish, for they were sweet and full of savor, and what was not eaten was dried and put aside against the winter.

We were severely punished if transgressions were discovered. At one point, directed to throw out some burned soup, I tried to scrape it into some sacking for transport to a work slave who was ailing. Jolietta found me at it and forced me to eat the cold, burned mass there and then before stringing me up for the lash. The food was the entirety of what I was given for the next three days.

I learned that in Tabat there were individuals known as Beast farmers – Humans who held the titles to Beasts by law but left the Beasts alone, to make their own way in the world or sometimes pay the farmer a weekly portion of their income.

Some did this out of the goodness of their hearts, while others chose to make their daily living in such a partnership, being too lazy or otherwise disinclined to keep the strict grasp that a slavekeeping arrangement would entail.

But for a Beast to belong to such a farmer, they must manage to save up a sum to give the farmer, with which to buy them – and this sum was inordinate indeed. Nonetheless, I began to put aside such small coins as fell my way.

Part VII

Visitors to the estate – My friendship with the Sphinx - I learn to read – I am trained as a physician – I escape and am caught – I father a number of children – I begin writing this account

Other creatures constantly passed in and out of Jolietta's kingdom, either in the process of being trained or nursed. I nursed litters of Dog-men and groomed Gryphons being trained for the Tabatian cavalry.

Many institutions sent their ailing Beasts to Jolietta for doctoring. The Sphinx had been purchased by the College of Mages, and when she fell prey to cough, the College sent her to Jolietta's farm to be nursed back to health with boxes of heated sand and horehound and pinetop tea. Jolietta allowed me to care for the Sphinx and over the month she spent there at Piper Hill, we became fast friends. Even after her departure, we passed messages back and forth as we could.

Jolietta thought me intelligent enough to absorb some knowledge of medicine. I learned to identify and pull bad teeth, to apply leeches, and to administer medicine to Beasts. She taught me the names and methods of the different preparations, and had me smell and taste each of them so I would know them in the future.

She said that if I learned quickly, she would be able to trust me with errands to outlying farms, to tend creatures too ill to be fetched to her.

As a result of learning such things, I taught myself to read and write, although my hand was poor and unpracticed. Still, I worked at improving my understanding of the art where I could, stealing pamphlets and magazines to read, hiding them away in a shed near the dragon pens.

I made it my practice not to speak much, but my mistress caught something suspicious in my demeanor and watched my actions jealously. Aware of the scrutiny, I took care to make no move that would confirm her fears. Indeed, I was a model slave, unobtrusive as a piece of furniture, quick to anticipate her wants and desires. I had feared that I might be put in a brothel, for the sailors on the ship said that most Beasts of my kind ended up under such circumstances. And to do her credit, Jolietta never spoke word or made gesture that led me to think she desired sexual congress with me.

Time wore on and I grew from my spindly youth to a broad-shouldered male. While Bebe had no interest in me, the same was not true for many of the centaur mares in the area, along with a few of the Human women. The dryads liked for me to kiss them, and stoke them with my hands, and we spent many hours in this wise, but the mares were what I ached for.

Jolietta forbade me congress, saying that the owners should have to pay well for my seed, but I managed to defy her more than once, and blame the outcome on my nature. Jolietta thought, as most Humans did, that Beasts were inevitable prey to their natures, and that I could not help taking an opportunity at congress with a mare in heat any more than I could help eating when I was hungry and food presented itself.

At first I tried to ensure that my loves produced no progeny, but when a mare is fertile, Nature takes its course and soon enough a child results. When I realized this, I attempted to deny myself such pleasures, but I was young and easily swayed by my body's yearnings. And so, within a few years, I had a number of colts, both purchased and gratis, in the surrounding area, and experienced the first pangs of seeing a child sold away from me, when a neighbor parted with mare and colt to a trader who took them northward to Verranzo's City.

Those who advocate slavery would deny such familial bonds. Surely they have never seen a mother, wailing and lashed by despair more harshly than any cat-o-nine-tails, trying in vain to reach to her infant! The child stands, uncertain and blinking, sensing the sorrow to come, and then is driven ever more frantic by his dam's remonstrations! More than once such a sight has torn with an eagle's claws at my heart.

After several years of study as a physician, Jolietta began to take me with her when she paid visits to check on animals, and I would administer medicine or treatments under her watchful eye. Several of the freeholders asked her if she meant to geld me, and she spoke forthrightly, saying that centaurs of good frame sold well, and that she reckoned she would have good fat breeding fees of me.

"Ain't you afraid that will leave him too feisty?" one demanded, and she shrugged.

"It would be a poor advertisement for my training skills if I did not trust in them," she said.

By the time she began to put me out to stud on a regular basis, my lost children ate at me. I saw their sad faces in my dreams at night, and whenever I encountered one of their mothers on a visit, I glimpsed only reproach in her eyes. What would it be like, I thought, to live in a place where I might be part of a herd. Where I might sire children and teach them as I had been taught, how to sing, how to wield a spear, how to count on cabi.

Driven by such fantasies, I entertained thoughts of escape. While passing through a farmhouse kitchen, I had the opportunity to steal a knife that had sat waiting to cut pieces of a ham. While I found out later that my theft caused a great hubbub, suspicion did not land on me. I kept my weapon out in the garden, tucked beneath a little-used bench, and waited a few weeks to make sure that no late suspicions would lead to Jolietta searching my chamber, as happened from time to time.

I put food aside, mainly oat rusks that I stole from the kitchen and dried apples given me by the work Beasts. I stitched a pack out of burlap stolen from the stable, and read through Jolietta's almanac to discover the next night when moonlight would be sufficient to see at night. I kept my eyes open for other items that would not be missed, hoping for a torch or lantern, but fate did not provide such.

I knew from reading the newspaper that if I made my way north to Verranzo's City, I might find souls willing to shelter me, and eventually send me west, where the Humans were few. I did not know much of the territory that lay in my way, but I figured I might head for the coast and then work my way up along it towards that haven.

Accordingly, I left late at night, creeping out from my quarters in the stable. Under the cover of darkness, I made my way along the deserted road to the place where its cliffs overlooked the sea, and then made my way north and east from there. In the hour when dawn fingered the sky, I found a patch of woodland between fields and sheltered in its depths – the lush grass testified that only deer and smaller wildlife came there. I found a bed beneath a fallen pine and slept, dreaming of freedom, among the smell of the rotting brown needles.

My hope was that in the morning, I would not be missed since Jolietta would think I had gone to slaughter game and feed the dragons. The day was bright and sunny, and would render the dragons torpid and unlikely to complain much – I had fed them early and more than their usual the day before, and they customarily gorged themselves and then did not eat for several days. And in those hours while I was not missed, traffic would pass back and forth along the road, muddling and – hopefully – destroying my scent so hounds would not be able to trace me to my hiding place.

I was far enough away from the road that I could not hear the traffic or conversation there, and while once or twice I thought I heard the baying of hounds, carried on the wind, I was never certain. When evening came and I could move in the shadows, hiding whenever I came across another traveler, I continued to move up along the coast.

I travelled in this way for three days, living off the rusks in my pouch and food stolen from gardens where I could. On the fourth night, I heard pursuit behind me and the cries of hounds, which grew louder and louder. Jolietta had anticipated my path and been waiting for it to coincide with her patrols. She tracked me into a ravine, where I slipped and slid in the clay and mud, unable to find traction. Cassius climbed down and tied me with ropes before he and Brutus drew me up out of the rocky cleft by means of pulleys.

The beating I had earned was a savage one indeed. Afterwards Jolietta let me hang by the wrists throughout the night. I lay insensible for two days afterward, and then resumed my duties.

Part VIII

From that point forward, I kept any thoughts of escape to myself. I was resolved that in the end, I would, but that next time I would be far better prepared. Jolietta kept a careful eye on me at first, but as the months wore into years, she relaxed her vigilance, assuming from my demeanor that I had capitulated to my captivity.

My life in general improved as a result of my quiet demeanor, for I was determined to betray no sign of my intended, inevitable rebellion to my mistress. Jolietta allowed me better food, and the cook instructed me in culinary techniques that I might find useful in tempting the appetite of a patient or the mistress at some point. I learned how to create trifles and frumenties, soufflés and omelets, and a variety of nogs and creams and soups of medicinal nature.

Where for many, years of interaction would engender trust, Jolietta grew more and more suspicious of my motives as time passed. She stopped sending me out on errands by myself, saying that I had fathered as many free colts as she cared me to, and she would no longer allow me in the still-room, where she kept her herbs and medicines, by myself.

Word came to me through other slaves that in Tabat one of the Human presses had devoted itself to the cause of abolition, and wished to receive accounts of the lives of Beasts, in order to speak on their behalf to those who insisted that they should remain subject, incapable of governing themselves. And so I sat down to write, and penned the first part of this tale and sent it by secret means to the newspaper.

A month later, by the same means in reverse, a newspaper arrived in my room. I unfolded its stiff pages and looked throughout its sections. On the fifth page, I found these words, beginning the dense blocks of print beneath an advertisement for decorative tiles: Like many of my fellow Beasts I was born to freedom, in a small village named Dekalion, a confluence of five centaur herds.

I continued writing my pages, but it was difficult to get candles in order to compose at night. I limited myself to one chapter each purple month, and used any extra luminescence to correct and edit my prose. I composed paragraphs while working for Jolietta making pills or feeding the dwarf dragons, and polished them as I sat eating or doing handiwork in the evenings.

I did not grow up believing in Gods, such as the Humans follow. And even now, when the Humans insist that everything is theirs, a gift from those Gods, I find myself dubious, though I know I might find myself slain for such words. The Humans do as they will, and firstly say that we are like infants who must be looked over and then say we are monsters who must be controlled, creatures incapable of rising above their natures, who will do wrong to them if we are allowed to be our own agents. And so I questioned these things, and asked my fellow Beasts if they did not question them as well.

Part IX
The aftermath

It is unknown how Fino's mistress discovered his activities, but on the day he was due to pass his next manuscript to his correspondent, it failed to arrive. The messenger stopped at Piper Hill to secretly ask after him, and was told that he was ill.

Subsequent queries learned that she had performed some surgery on him that robbed him of the majority of his intelligence, rendering him able to feed and tend himself, but little else, and that shortly thereafter he had been sold to a passing trader, and taken to the Old Continent.

His fate is unknown as of this writing. The last piece of his narrative was smuggled out, but the hand is illegible and hurried, and only the first sentence can be read.

It says only this: "I am determined to disobey."

Section 2
Ways Into Stories: Fragments

CHAPTER 6
CHARACTERS

What it is

These stories begin with a character or set of characters: distinct figures or personalities, sometimes taken from history, legend, mythology, or other cultural source. Your approach will differ according to whether it's a single character or a set; I'll talk about both.

Characters are innately interesting because they are people, and human beings like to watch other human beings, particularly ones who are unaware of the observation. We like to see what people do when confronted with specific problems, perhaps because we hope to learn second-hand from their experience. Most of us enjoy people-watching to one degree or another, and if we are able to do it while unobserved ourselves by the object of our scrutiny, all the better. That is, perhaps, at the root of fiction's enjoyability.

The point of view character is the vehicle through which your reader experiences the story. Figure out what will be enjoyable or memorable during the experience and make it more so for your reader.

What it provides

With a character, you know the personality or personalities involved, which helps you know what they want, as well as how they might or might not go about achieving those wants.

With a set of characters you know the relationships as well as the personalities. You have some sense of the conflicts, how what one character wants collides with another's desires.

You probably have some sense of the world. People exist in a world and are shaped by it. How has your character been influenced by their surroundings?

You probably have some sense of the tone. Is it comic, dramatic, mysterious...? What emotions does your character evoke in you, and how can you make your reader feel the same way?

Considerations

Your character's backhistory, the things that have happened to them before the story ever starts, may well shape the events that you are writing about. Take a little time to figure out the basics of their existence: roughly how old they are, what are the important ties of family or friends in their life, what their life has been like and how that experience has shaped their attitude towards life.

Similarly, what resources does your character have available to them? How willing are they to use up those resources (and can you add tension by making that part of their internal struggle)? That includes social resources—who owes them a favor? (And who are they dodging because they owe a favor?)

Look at the relationships they have with other characters. What are the moments that have built those relationships? How have they adapted themselves to the other character or characters?

Pitfalls

Think about the relationship between the character and the world. How do they relate to their surroundings: do they trust the world or are they suspicious of everything? How do they make their living and how does that affect their way of thinking?

Too many characters? I find that I often have a cast of thousands in early drafts, all of which can be trimmed down. Think about what specific purposes a character serves in the story and see where you can double up, combine, or even eliminate.

Next steps

Make sure you understand what the main character wants. What they want determines the overall movement of their actions, perhaps even some of the day to day actions as well. What they want helps you know what the plot is about.

Along the same lines, make sure you understand the forces that are keeping your main character from getting what they want. This also will help you know what the plot is about.

Exercises

1. Do a scene set: showing your character preparing/eating/cleaning up after a meal; your character getting ready to sleep/sleeping/waking; your character earning or spending money. OA: Do them all.
2. Describe three objects that your character uses daily, describing them from your character's point of view.
3. What is one secret your character is hiding from the world? It doesn't have to be a big one. Write a scene that involves the secret: either the moment of its creation, a moment where your character reveals it to another character, or a moment where another character tries unsuccessfully to get them to reveal it.

Case study: (Vocobox)

I've chosen an odd story for the case study, my story "Vocobox," which originally appeared in *Twisted Cat Tales*. The impetus was my cat, whose name is Raven, and who was extremely talkative. I started wondering what would happen if he had limited speech. In truth, the story is actually about his owner and her reaction to the change in the cat and what it reveals to her about her husband's infidelity.

The story started by writing the beginning and was one where the story unfolded as I wrote my way into it. I wondered why the husband had chosen to make the cat talk, and explored the reaction of both to the failure of the attempt.

This is an early story, and I don't know that the ending is all it could be. It is, however, extremely true to life where the cat is concerned.

Vocobox

Ever since my husband installed a Vocobox ™ in our cat in a failed experiment, he (the cat, not my husband) stands outside the closed bedroom door in the mornings, calling. The intelligence update was partially successful, but the only word the cat has learned is its own name, Raven, which he uses to convey everything. I hear him when I wake up, the sound muted by the wooden door between us.

"Raven. Raven. Raven." Beside me, Lloyd murmurs something and turns over, tugging the sheet away, the cold whispering me further awake. When I go out to feed the cat, his voice lowers as he twines around my ankles, words lapsing into purrs. He butts against my legs with an insistent anxiousness, waiting for the dish to be filled. "Raven. Raven." Kibble poured, I move to make our own breakfast, turning on the coffee maker and listening to its preparatory burble.

"I don't know what I expected," my husband mutters as he drinks his coffee in hasty gulps. "That cat was never very smart for a cat." He glares at Raven as though blaming him for the failures of the world at large. The Vocobox is his own invention; his company hopes to market it this fall, and a promotion may hinge upon it. The last laurels my husband won are wearing thin; if the Vocobox is a success, he'll be able to rest a while longer.

But when he first proposed installing it in the cat, he didn't say it was still experimental. "The kids are gone, and you need some company," he'd said. "The cat loves you best anyhow; now you can talk to him, and he'll talk back." He gave me a slight smirk and an eyebrow curve that implied that without him I'd be a dotty old cat lady, living in a studio apartment that smelled of pee and old newspapers.

"I'll be late again tonight," he tells me now. "And when I'm concentrating, I've found leaving my cell off helps. If you need something, just leave a message. Or call the service, that's what we pay them for." He's out the front door before I can reply.

Every morning seems the same nowadays. My husband's heels, exiting. The immaculate lawn outside. On Thursdays, the housekeeping service remotely activates the grass cutting robot. I see it out there, sweeping through the fresh spring grass that never grows high enough to hide it. A plastic sheep, six inches tall, sits atop its round metal case, someone's idea of creative marketing. But the robot is done within the hour and then things are the same again. Back in the box.

I go into the living room, activate the wall viewer, and lose myself in reality television, where everyone has eventful lives. Soon Raven curls up on my lap. "Raven," he murmurs, and begins to purr.

The mouths of the people on the screen move, but the words that come out are meaningless, so I hit the mute button. Now the figures collide and dance on the screen; every life is more interesting than my own.

At noon, I push the cat off my lap and have a sandwich; at dinner time a hot meal appears in the oven. I take it out myself, pour a glass of Chardonnay, take the bottle to the table with me. When did I become this boring person? At college, I studied music, was going to sing opera. I sang in a few productions, fell in love, became a trophy wife, and produced two perfect trophy children who are out there now, perpetuating the cycle. All those voice lessons wasted.

On the EBay channel that night I look for a hobby. There's knitting, gardening, glass-blowing, quilling... too many to choose from. I remember quilling from my daughter's Bluebird days. We curled bits of paper, glued them down in decorative patterns on tiny wooden boxes. What was the point? I drink a little more wine before I go to sleep.

When he comes to bed, my husband snuggles up, strokes my arm. He murmurs something inaudible, the tone conveying affection. This only happens when he feels guilty. From the recently showered smell of him, I know what he feels guilty about. This must be an assistant I haven't met yet.

When I don't speak, he says "What's the matter, cat got your voice box?" He chortles to himself at his clever joke before he lapses into sleep, not pursuing my silence. Out in the living room, I hear the cat wandering. "Raven."

"You're like a cliché," my husband says at breakfast. "Desperate housewife. Can't you find something to do?"

The cat's attention swivels between us, his green eyes wide and pellucid with curiosity. "Raven?" he says in an interrogative tone.

I watch my husband's heels, the door closing behind them, the deliberately good-humored but loud click, once again.

"Raven," the cat says as it looks up at me, its voice shaded with defiance.

"Dora," I say to the cat. I'm tired and sore as though I'd been beaten. The room wavers with warmth and weariness.

"Raven."

"Dora."

"Raven."

"Dora."

I can't help but laugh as he watches my face, but he is not amused as I am; his tail lashes from side to side although every other inch of him is still.

Online, I look at the ads. Nannies, housekeepers, maids...I am a cliché. I embrace my inanity. Desperate housewife indeed, being cheated on by an aging husband who isn't even clever enough to conceal it. This is my reality. But if I explain it, I start the avalanche down into divorce. I'll end up living in a box on the street, while my husband will remarry, keep living in this expensive, well-tended compound. I've seen it happen to other women.

"Raven," the cat says with tender grace, interposing himself in front of the monitor. Facing me, he puts his forehead against the top of my chest, pressing firmly. "Raven," he whispers.

Sunday, while my husband's out playing golf, the phone keeps ringing. "Caller's name undisclosed," the display says. And when I pick it up, there is only silence on the other end. The third time I say "He's out playing golf and has his cell phone turned off, because it distracts him. Call back this evening." and hang up.

He scuttles out in the evening after another of the calls, saying he needs to go into work, oversee a test run. Later that night, he curls against me, smelling of fresh soap. Outside the door, Raven is calling.

"Another cat would take the implant better," my husband says. "I'll get a kitten and we'll try that."

"No," I tell him. "He's too old to get used to a new kitten in the house. It will just upset him."

"I'm trying to do something nice for you."

"Buy the other woman a kitten," I say, even as dire predictions scream through my mind, commanding me to silence. "Buy her dozens. I'm sticking with this one."

He rolls over, stunned and quiet. For the rest of the night, I lie there. Outside, the night continues, limitless. I pass the time imagining what I will do. Nannying is, I hear, pleasant work. I'll sing the babies lullabies.

He's silent in the morning as well. In the light of day as we sit facing each other across the Formica table, I reach down to extend my hand to the cat, who arches his back and rubs against my fingertips.

"We need to talk," Lloyd finally demands.

"Dora," I say.

"What?"

"Dora. Dora, Dora." I rise to my feet and stand glaring at him. If I had a tail, it would lash back and forth like an annoyed snake, but all my energy is focused on speaking to my husband.

"Is that supposed to be funny?"

"Dora. Dora. Dora." I almost sob the words out, as emotions clutch at my throat with an insistent clutch, trying to mute me, but I force the words past the block, out into the open air. We stand like boxers, facing each other in the squareness of the ring.

Lloyd moves to the door, almost backing away. His eyes are fixed on my lips; every time I say my name,his expression flickers, as though the word has surprised him anew.

"We can talk about this later," he says. The door closes behind him with a click of finality.

What can I do? I settle on the couch and the cat leaps up to claim my lap, butts his head against my chin. He lapses into loud purrs, so loud I can feel the vibration against my chest, quivering like unspoken words. He doesn't say anything, but I know exactly what he means.

CHAPTER 7

DIALOGUE

What it is

Dialogue is a subset of writing from a character or set of characters, a conversation that is taking place between two or more people. Instead of seeing the people, you're hearing the voices, and what's more, you're hearing conversations in which they interact. Dialogue takes place in a specific moment, and provides you with information about what's going on as well as the people engaged in the dialogue.

What it provides

Dialogue gives you a sense of the flavor of the story. Voices reflect their culture and their world, through diction, vocabulary, and other distinct elements.

Dialogue gives you a sense of the speakers' personalities. Not just the protagonist, but the characters with whom they are interacting.

Dialogue tells you things about the relationships between the speakers, particularly the power dynamic, and which has more/less power.

Dialogue can tell you something about the setting if it is distinctive enough to be associated with a specific culture or location.

Good dialogue can make a story really come alive for a reader, as though the conversation were going on right there at their elbow. There is something innately fascinating about eavesdropping, and part of it is the fascination of trying to construct the narrative to match what's being said in your head—a task any reader is already engaging in.

Considerations

What parts are missing? What things about the story aren't supplied by the dialogue? If they're generic, for example, you may want to consider a specific setting. You'll need to go back over the dialogue at some point and make sure that it fits with the setting that you have selected.

What is the flavor created by the dialogue and how do you make the rest of the story match?

Pitfalls

Your characters aren't really talking about anything. They're just saying hello or goodbye, and not really much else. Unless the meeting or farewell is something that's very significant—the parting of two lovers, the reunion of sisters after a decade, a teacher saying goodbye to a student about to go off into space—it may need a lot of expansion to become the story.

Only one person is talking. This is a monologue rather than a dialogue. In this case, you may be better off looking at who is speaking and using them as the starting point for a character-based approach to the idea.

Your dialogue is the story. Is your story a joke or anecdote that someone is telling another person? If so, is that frame really necessary, or should you go a little deeper into the story and tell it more directly, rather than giving it secondhand, which can create distance between a story and a reader?

Next steps

What sort of scene does the dialogue take place in, and what does the scene accomplish? Is it an introductory scene, intended to let the reader get to know the character? Is it later on in the story, moving the plot along? Or does it happen at the end and help tie everything up—in which case find out what's being tied up and create the other end of it.

What does the dialogue tell you about what each character wants? Are they expressing a direct desire or is it, as is more likely, hidden somewhere underneath their words?

What does the dialogue tell you about the power relationship(s) between the characters? Rarely are two characters at the same power level, although they may each have power over the other in different ways. How is the power dynamic being played out between the two of them?

Exercises

1. Imagine the scene from the point of view of an onlooker who cannot hear what the other characters are saying. Write a description of the action from their point of view. OA version: try this with both a disinterested onlooker and someone who has a strong interest in what's happening.
2. Write one of the characters recounting the conversation to a third character. What points of it do they include and exclude? OA version: Figure out a point about the conversation that the first character is trying not to let the third character know about.
3. Look at the conversation. What isn't being said? Write down the assumptions that are implicit in the dialogue: Case has the gun, Case doesn't want to give him the gun, the gun is loaded. Do any of these create points that may need to be expanded upon earlier or later in the story? OA: Write an account of the scene from a point of view that is utterly alien and doesn't understand the majority of what's going on.

Case study: (The Coffee Cup Song)

For this case study, I've chosen another early story, "The Coffee Cup Song," which hinges on a repeated phrase that happens in dialogue as well as the song that the narrator writes. It plays a little with country and western music tropes, and it began with the idea of a girl writing a song that reflects her life, and her mother's objection to having the personal events of her life included in the song.

I let the tone of the dialogue, which I found evocative of those country and western songs, be the guiding impetus of the story, which had to be one about a cheating husband and his comeuppance.

The Coffee Cup Song

How dare you!" my momma says, her voice high and screeching like a lonely fiddle. "How dare you!" She throws one two three four five coffee cups at me. Percussion smash. Tinkle of white shards on the blue linoleum. We'll be drinking coffee out of styrofoam for a while, I think. That's all we have, coffee cup-wise, except for the sixth one, the last thing my daddy drank out of the morning he left, and it's sitting in the china cabinet in the front room.

She doesn't aim to hit me, although the fifth cup comes close. It explodes on the floor and a chip dings off my guitar's gloss. She's never thrown anything at me before. I watch the way you might watch a television program showing animals doing something you've never seen them do.

"How dare you!" my mother says again. She sinks down in her chair and puts her head in her hands. Her words are muffled as they make their way past the blue sleeves of her workshirt, the one with "Candy" embroidered in red loops on the front pocket. "How dare you put me in that song?"

I don't answer. She'll cry for a while, and then she'll sweep up the pieces, wipe her face with a cool rag, and go to work at the Krave-More Diner, where you can get the finest cup of coffee in this town or any other. I put my guitar in its case, go out the screen door, and head out down the road, raising puffs of red dust puffs around my heels.

It's morning. Maybe too early to have sprung it on her, when she was still shaking off her dreams. The sky arches over me high and sweet, and I can hear the sighing of mourning doves and the wind in the telephone wires. The air's cool now, but it'll heat up later, till you don't feel much like moving more than your hand on the guitar neck as you sit on the porch swing and try to puzzle out a song or maybe just that chorus that's been eluding you, chasing it up and down the frets. Back home, my momma's washing her face. She knows I'm not going far.

I can't say how I came by my love of honkytonk music. We always listened to classical at my house, enough so I can call up some of the pieces in my mind, the big booming ones that go with the Kansas prairie. But a lot of that stuff's too tinkly and quick. When you're driving down the road, the notes fly out the window and bury themselves in the long grass. They don't stick around and keep you company, the way honkytonk music does.

I taught myself to play on my daddy's guitar, the only thing he left behind besides that coffee cup. At first my hands were too small and soft to do much more than strum, but they toughened up. I learned to pick fast and easy and the music sounded so lovely, I kept stopping to say to myself, is that me, is that me that's making those fine sounds?

My name is J.D. Daniels, Jennifer Delilah if you must know, but I go by J.D., the way my daddy did. I don't mean to make it sound like he's dead, because he isn't. My daddy sold insurance and provided for us for eight years. Then a wander itch came on him like a night fever and he packed up his things and left us without a word. Didn't take him overly far, though. He's living over in Greensborough with a woman named Amanda who's cleaned up his act. He doesn't drink or run around any more, and wears a tie to church every Sunday.

The only present he ever gave me was that guitar, an old steel string no name brand, and I don't know if the gift was intentional. I came off better than my momma. All she has is a cup.

My momma works at the Krave-More. She brings folks coffee and smiles at them to sweeten up their day. She's slow to smile, but when she does, it could melt ice from across the room.

I'll be fourteen next month. Changes coming, my grandma tells me. I know all that stuff. We learned it in health class and there's no call for her to nod so mysteriously. But I don't tell her that. She means well by us, and helps out when she can. The house we're living in belongs to her, and every birthday, she and I dress up in our best and go down to the First Farmers' Bank and deposit my birthday check in my savings account for college. People ask me what I want to be when I grow up, and I tell them an archaeologist or a country singer or an astrophysicist, but the fact of the matter is that I don't know. But I pray every night to grow up a good woman like my momma and grandma, and not to be afflicted with a wander itch.

Three months ago I wrote a song. That's what caused all the trouble. The music teacher, Miss Mopp, told us about a contest sponsored by a radio station in Abilene, Kansas. You wrote a song and sent it in, you singing along with whatever instrument suited your fancy. The radio station would pick the best tape and the winner would come in and record it at their studio. Then they'd make 45 rpm records of it to give away to five hundred lucky souls and play it three times daily on the air.

I thought that sounded pretty easy. I've been writing songs ever since I started playing guitar. At first I had a hard time getting them out of my head and into the strings. But I got better. I'd listen in the evenings to the songs on the radio, and I'd fool around until I figured out how so and so got that lonesome sound or how somebody else did that fancy bridge. I'd play a song over fifty, sixty times, until I got it right, but I had to play soft, because my momma hated what I was playing.

"That's trash music," she'd snort. "Learn to play something higher tone and I'll pay for guitar lessons. Better yet, we'll rent a piano, and you can play all day."

But by then, I knew enough to play the songs I loved, sad songs that crept out my window and spread across the sky like a million twinkling stars, sorrowful songs about cheating men and hearts worn out with weeping. I could make tears run down my grandma's cheeks when I played, and there's no higher tribute she could pay, but my momma stayed dry- eyed.

Miss Mopp let me borrow the school tape recorder. I played three songs, then rewound and listened. My first song was about that coffee cup in our front room and it was so sad it made the soles of my feet itch

But I wasn't sure. One time I wrote a song about being buried in white roses, because they're the most romantic things I know. I thought it was a sad song, but my grandma only laughed. Another time I wrote a song about a single candle in the window, and I thought that was a sad song, but my grandma paid it no mind. This song seemed sad, but I couldn't test it out on my mother, seeing as how she figured in it, which might influence her judgement. My grandma wasn't handy, and I wanted to turn the song in the next day.

I went ahead and wrote my name, age and school down on a recipe card with a little drawing of jam pots and squash up in the corner, because we didn't have any index cards. I gave it to Miss Mopp. And then I forgot about it, and that's the pure and simple truth, until yesterday when Miss Mopp told me I'd won.

I thought my momma would be pleased when I told her the news at breakfast. And she was, at first, until I fetched down my guitar and played that song for her. And that's when coffee cups started flying through the air.

Iwalkdowntheroadtomygrandma'shouse.She'supandinherkitchen. "Sit down and play me this prize-winning song," she says when I get in the doorway. That's how I know my momma has already called her on the telephone. This is where I go when things get a little hard every now and then. My grandma pours me a glass of milk and puts two chocolate doughnuts on a plate. I sit down, prop my guitar on my knee, and play her that song. She starts crying before the first verse's halfway through, stands there and dabs at her eyes with her apron when I finish.

"That's the saddest song I ever heard," she says. "I can see where it'd fetch a prize or two. But do you understand why your momma's so upset, J.D. honey?"

I shake my head.

"It's just a song."

"But it's your momma's song. It's all her sadness spread out in the air for anyone to hear," she says, blowing her nose. "And maybe there's folks she doesn't want listening."

I know she's right. But I wanted to write a song about the saddest thing I knew, and that coffee cup has always qualified.

"It's my song too," I say to my grandma. "I live there too."

My momma doesn't say anything about the song at dinner. I figure she'll ignore it, the way she does with things she doesn't like. She doesn't say anything at all to me.

Two days later, my grandma drives me into Abilene to the radio station. We figure we'll record the song in the morning, then have lunch, go visit the Greyhound Hall of Fame and the house Dwight D. Eisenhower was born in. It's a scorching day by the time we get there, but the radio station, WKNS, your station for Kansas country sound, is air conditioned.

They take me in a room full of fancy dials and buttons. They make me play the song on my guitar, and then they play it back through headphones and I sing along with what I played. I play and sing maybe ten, twelve times before the way it sounds satisfies the man sitting up in the booth drinking coffee. He shakes my hand and congratulates me. His voice is thick and there's a little bit of water in the corners of his eyes. He says "That's the saddest song I ever heard. Thanks for letting me listen."

A secretary gives me papers to sign, which my grandma reads through first, and then a lady DJ takes me in her office to tape an intro. It's like being inside a big machine, full of toggle switches and dials. She's got pictures of singers taped up on the walls: Patsy Cline, Kitty Wells, Loretta Lynn.

"Just speak naturally, sugar," she tells me. She flips a button on her microphone. "So tell me, J.D., how old are you?"

I tell her, and she asks questions like where I go to school and what's my favorite class and how I learned to play the guitar. Then she says "How did you write that song?"

I take a minute before I answer, "It's a song about a member of my immediate family, but if you please, I'd rather not say anything more."

She studies me, and flips the switch off, but she doesn't ask me any more about the circumstances of the song.

My grandma buys me lunch. We stroll around town and visit the Greyhound Hall of Fame. Eisenhower's house is closed, so all we do is walk around the outside and look in the windows, which is about as interesting as you'd expect. My grandma gives me a present she's made, a shirt with "J.D. Daniels: Prizewinning Songwriter" embroidered on the front pocket. I know I'll never wear it to school, but I like the way it looks, and I thank her. I wrap it up again, carefully, and keep it on my lap as we bounce our way home over dusty roads.

When I get back to our house, nothing's changed. My momma won't speak to me much. Meals are awfully quiet. She buys new coffee cups, the same as the old ones. They start playing my song on WKNS, and mail me five of the records. Some of the kids at school tell me they heard my song and say they liked it. But I don't turn the radio at home to WKNS because I'm afraid if my mother hears what I said on the radio, it'll make things worse.

Two days later, I come home from school, and there's my daddy sitting on the front porch. He stands as I come up toward the house. I squint against the sun like I can't make out who he is.

"Jennifer, is that you?" he says, and before I can nod or shake my head, he picks me up and hugs me tight. I hold myself stiff.

"It's me, baby, it's your daddy," he says and puts me down. I look at him real hard, this being the first chance I've had in a number of years, but I don't say anything. I don't know what to say.

"I heard your song on the radio," he says. "That's the saddest song I've ever heard. It touched my heart and showed me how I done wrong by your momma. I've come back to the both of you, and you can take that coffee cup out of the cupboard, wash it out, and fill it up again for me."

That's a quote from my song, but it sounds different coming from him.

"You'll have to wait out here till Momma comes home," I tell him and his face falls, but then he smiles even bigger.

"Tell you what I'm gonna do," he says, leaning forward and whispering like we were spies in a movie. "I'm gonna go buy your momma some flowers. I'll be back in half an hour."

My momma comes home before the dust from his wheels has settled. She sits down at the kitchen table and I pour her a cup of the coffee I have waiting. I don't know how to say what's happened. I study on ways to do it. She leans back in her chair and puts her feet up, kicking her shoes clear across the room. She's still not talking to me much.

He knocks before I get the chance. I follow her to the front door, and there he is on his knees, with a big bunch of red roses. He says, "Candy honey, I've come back to you."

She stares down at him through the wire squares of the screen. I donUt remember his shirt so white, his blue eyes shining, his hair slicked back and shiny. The roses are full open, petals sagging in the heat, sending up a sweet sad smell.

"Jennifer's song on the radio touched my heart and made me see how I done wrong by you and her." He smiles up at her. His hair on top is just about gone, and the skin gleams between the strands in the sunlight. He rocks a little, as though the wood under his knees was paining him.

"Does Amanda know you're here?" she asks.

"Amanda and I, we're past history," he says. He smooths his hand through the air. "Water under the bridge."

She steps back and looks over at me. I shrug, trying to say this wasn't what I wrote that song for. I wrote it for the sake of writing a song, not so he'd hear it. She shrugs back. He kneels outside in silence, watching us.

My momma looks uncertain at first, but the edges of her mouth quirk up a touch. She turns around, opens the door of the china cupboard, and takes the coffee cup, that goddamned coffee cup, out. I hold my breath.

"I believe you left this last time you were here," she says as politely as if she were on a commercial, and opens the door enough to hold out the cup. He takes it with a funny grin on his face and starts to speak. My momma closes the door on him and goes back into the kitchen. I follow her. She sits down at the table and adds more coffee to her cup to warm it up. A car door slams outside.

"J.D. honey," she says to me. "Go get your guitar and play that song for me. I believe I'm feeling more reconciled to it."

CHAPTER 8

SETTING

What it is

Sometimes you know the world in which a story takes place. Usually this is the result of a particularly unusual aspect of the setting. For example:

- Everyone in the world is made of a particular substance.
- The world is a rotating slice of a Dyson sphere, built by an ancient civilization. (Larry Niven's *Ringworld*)
- Water falls out of the air onto the person whenever anyone lies. (John Chu's "*The Water That Falls From Nowhere*")

It might also be a setting that is familiar for a particular reason, perhaps because it is an actual physical place or because it is featured in some cultural work.

What it provides

Settings give you a wealth of physical and sensory details, things that you can use to build an experience for the reader that feels genuinely and satisfyingly speculative.

Settings can give you great eyeball kicks. “Eyeball kicks,” a term taken from the Turkey City Lexicon and attributed to Rudy Rucker, are “vivid, telling details that create a kaleidoscopic effect of swarming visual imagery against a baroquely elaborate SF background.” I tend to think of them more as nifty squee details, little touches that entertain, delight, and amaze through a presentation that is strongly engaging in a sensory way, primarily visual.

Pitfalls

Sometimes the setting is more generic than you think. For example, “a world where superheroes exist” takes more thought than showing a newspaper headline that says, “Ms. Liberty Saves the Universe.” Superheroes would have a massive impact on the economy, the culture, and law enforcement, for one. Make your world idiosyncratic and wonderful. This is something worth putting a little time and thought into, although I wouldn’t let it delay you too much in the story’s construction. Take a walk or ride for an hour or two, spend it thinking about the story, and you should have more than enough of the details that make something yours. If you’ve ever run a tabletop roleplaying game, this is where you’re creating the flavor of your world, figuring out names of things and places and people, and what day to day life is like. What would you need to tell your players, and how can you do the same for your reader in a story?

Sometimes there just is no plot attached. Your world is ultra-cool, it is beautiful, but you cannot imagine what is going to happen over the course of the story. In the case, you’ve got a lot of work ahead of you. How do you know when this is happening? It’s when you’re drawing a complete blank every time you sit down to write this piece. There’s three possible approaches to it. One, you can leave it alone and let it steep in the murky inner tea of your subconscious. At some point, perhaps years down the line, it will emerge, dripping but sufficiently infused with mental energy (have I stretched this metaphor far enough yet?) for you to write it down. Two, you can try pantsing your way into it, by which I mean, you sit down and write something inspired by the world—doesn't matter what—in timed writings, where you're focusing more on producing words than what's actually emerging—over and over until you find your sense of direction. Three, you steal a plot from elsewhere and use it (this is as valid as the first two approaches).

Considerations

Flesh out some of the implications. If it's primarily water, think about what sorts of forms the homes of its inhabitants might take. Spend some time daydreaming about it—this is a useful aspect of insomnia, if you can manage to start thinking about your stories instead of whatever else is keeping you awake, and you may even find it a good way to tune your mind's frenzy down a notch. Just remember that if you think of something important. you really should rouse yourself enough to scribble down enough to remember it by. Otherwise all you will remember in the morning is that you had a really good idea whose details now elude you, and that is very frustrating.

What are the economics of the setting? At the most basic level: what is scarce, and what is plentiful? This affects everything. Is it a world where metal is scarce? Every aspect of the cultures within it will be shaped by that scarcity, sometimes overtly, sometimes very subtly. What do people buy and sell and what is considered everyone's? On a world the air is free; on a spaceship that may not be the case.

How do you make it real, a place that engages all the reader's senses? Think about the setting at a particular moment when you're daydreaming, What are the transitory things about it: the salt on the breeze that wafts by, the wavering cry of a gull overhead, a profusion of spring azaleas. Those are the things that really convince a reader that you the author were there on some level, not in reality but in spirit at least. I keep these sorts of details in a notebook when I notice them, and may use one of those bits to inspire the back-formation of a world in which to write.

What are the problems implicit in the setting? What are the dangers that would affect your character, but more importantly what are the obstacles to them getting what they want?

Why choose that particular setting? There should be some reason to pick this setting over any other; it must matter to the story and be more than ornamentation. In "Five Ways to Fall in Love on Planet Porcelain," I imagined a world where everyone is made of porcelain. Because I wanted that threat of breaking, something that could be physical as well as spiritual, in a story about someone's collision with Love.

Next steps

Find your plot. Do you have one? If not, how can you get one that works well with the setting?

Slice into the world. Write a scene or two with as much sensory stuff as you can get into it, preferably a scene that you're not planning on using in the eventual story, so you'll feel less pressure in constructing it. (You are welcome to use it in your piece if you decide you want to; it's not uncommon to start writing a scene intended not to go in and find it emerging as something that needs to be included in the story.)

Exercises

1. Describe a local landmark or notable feature, including its economic impact, in 100-250 words. OA: Do this for 500-1000 words and/or include more than one landmark.
2. Presumably your setting includes a culture, a backdrop of living, interacting, presumably intelligent beings. Do a five minute timed writing detailing the contents of one of those inhabitant's pockets (or pouch, or traveling luggage, or whatever everyday item container you like). Overachiever version: Repeat for distinct castes within the culture, such as someone in the military, someone who is an educator, someone who is a beggar or other form of indigent, someone who is well-off financially.

3. How is your setting different from a generic version of whatever it is? What transitory details can you include, details that are particular to the moment, such as a flock of geese honking their way across the sky or a spring breeze perfumed with pear blossom?

Case study: (In The Lesser Southern Isles)

I've attached "In the Lesser Southern Isles." In its case, the impetus behind the story was a call for speculative pirate stories that I'd seen. I had been writing in Tabat for quite some time and thought I would write the story of someone's abduction by pirates. So I began with Lucy walking past the Piskie Wood, which had been featured in "The Bumblety's Marble" during a Tabatian sunset:

> *It was one of those Tabatian evenings when the sky is so blue that it throbs. The shadows swell and the sunlight, darkening to orange, takes on an expectant, waiting look. Lucy had been admiring new silks down on Thimble Street and one had been the same deep blue as the sky. She'd never get the silk—the youngest of four got second and third-me-downs – but she could dream a blue dress piped with narrow black lace bands.*
>
> *She heard the footsteps a few paces behind her as she turned into Stumble Lane but didn't take much notice.*
>
> *A few blocks ahead, a lamplighter's distant golden flicker moved from pole to pole. The shuttered houses here were set close together in precise, two-storied arrays. Only a few lights gleamed, scattered in arched lower windows. To the left loomed the high iron fence surrounding the Piskie Wood, caging tree trunks damp with the same rain that misted the slick cobblestones underfoot. She slowed to look upward, arrested by the contrast of dark leaves against cobalt.*

Thinking about bits of the world that had emerged in other stories let me construct their destination, a place which had featured in my other speculative pirate story, "Sugar." I knew they were roughly modeled on the islands supplying the Americas with sugar, spices, and rum in the 19th century, but I wanted them to have their own mysteries, including a mysterious zone that few dared sail—and which, of course, would be their destination.

This story has actually shaped the fantasy quartet I've been working on—Lucy emerges there in a slightly different form in *Hearts of Tabat*, and is crucial to the events of the final volume, *Gods of Tabat*.

In the Lesser Southern Isles

It was one of those Tabatian evenings when the sky is dark, pulsing blue. The shadows swelled and the sunlight, darkening to orange, took on an expectant, waiting look.

Lucy had been admiring new silks down on Thimble Street. One had been the same cobalt as the sky. She'd never get the silk—the youngest of four got second and third-me-downs. But she could dream a blue dress piped with black lace bands as much as she wanted to.

She heard the footsteps behind her as she turned into Stumble Lane but didn't take much notice.

A few blocks ahead, a lamplighter's distant golden flicker moved from pole to pole. The shuttered houses here were set close together in precise, two-storied arrays. Only a few lights gleamed, scattered in arched lower windows. To the left loomed the high iron fence surrounding Piskie Wood, caging tree trunks damp with the same rain that slick-misted the cobblestones underfoot. She slowed to look upward, arrested by the contrast of black leaves against the sunset's last efforts.

The footsteps approached in a rush and two men grabbed her from both sides, each taking an upper arm and rushing her along, continuing her movement down the street. They had no trouble lifting her. Even for a fifteen year old, she was small.

"Not a word, you, if you know what's good for yeh," one growled, his voice husky with tobacco and spirits. He shifted his grip and something sharp prodded her ribs.

“Hey!” a voice shouted behind them.

“Egga’s wounds!” the other man said. “Didntcha have a lookout earlier?”

They were running. She half-lurched, half-flew, gasping for breath whenever her feet touched the ground. As they passed a house, curtains twitched aside and a woman looked out. For one horrified moment, their eyes met before Lucy was dragged on. Their pursuer was still running after them, yelling.

“In here!” She was pulled into an alleyway, pushed into one man’s arms while his partner turned to meet the chaser, raising his arm and the club it held.

She would have paid more attention to his actions if it hadn’t been for her own problems. With expert quickness, the other man thrust a wadded rag into her mouth despite her struggles. He tied it in place before dropping a sack, smelling of burlap and horse manure, over her and hoisting her over his shoulder.

“Got her.”

“Yeah, what should I do with this ‘un?”

“Grab it, Cap’s always wanting more canaries.”

A house alarm’s vigorous clang came from somewhere and a woman shouted “Guards, guards!”

“Frith’s fingerlashings! Come on, this way.”

She couldn’t free her arms, bound painfully to her sides, so tightly she could hardly breathe. She jounced on her captor’s bony shoulder, trying to work her jaws free.

The shouting quieted behind them.

She was thrown onto something. Helpless, impotent, she kicked out, colliding with a wooden wall. Straw itch overtook her and she sneezed despite the gag, half-retching as she fought the cloth in her mouth. There was a jolt as something else was thrown in beside her and the world rumbled into action.

The ride was uncomfortable but brief. She could tell they were heading downhill towards the docks. Inside the musty sack, she could smell nothing, but when the cart rattled to a stop and she was pulled out, the cold breeze through the burlap confirmed her deduction.

"Please," she tried to shout despite the gag but to no avail. Hands grabbed and spun her. She was hoisted again on a shoulder, this time broader and more padded. It stepped forward and she felt the giddy sway underfoot.

A boat, she thought, we're on a boat.

She strained her ears but the bag's material muffled sound. There was clumping, and then she was out of the colder air and someplace warmer.

Her legs almost buckled as she was set on her feet and the bag pulled away with a rasp of rough cloth. A knife flashed and the gag fell away. She licked her dry lips and swallowed.

She found herself in a small cabin lit by guttering gilt lanterns set in pairs beside the doorway and reflected in the rounded mirrors on the opposite wall. The plushy carpet's color was peacock feather brilliant.

Space was at a premium here but every inch had been used. A desktop folded down from the wall on brass chains, its shelf rimmed to prevent objects from rolling off in rough seas and a bookcase had been set into one wall, jammed with worn volumes in motley assemblage beside a map holder whose round holes were filled with paper and parchment rolls. The only excess was the bed, which was wide enough for two and spilled with bead-bright, lozenge-shaped cushions. Like the desk and shelves, it had a railing edging it, presumably to keep the occupants contained during storms.

A carved wooden chair sat in the middle, a man perched on it. He leaned forward to glare at her, arms folded.

"This," he said in dubious tones, "is the Pot King's son, the College of Mages' prize?"

"He's in disguise, we thinks, Cap'n," one man said. "At the taverns we asked at, they said he likes to disguise hisself."

Lucy stole a glance over her shoulder. Her captors stood on either side of the door. Movement drew her eye downward: legs in unremarkable grey trousers and worn boots that twitched as though her stare had awakened them lay protruding from another burlap bag.

A cough returned her attention to the man before her.

"I am Captain Jusef Miryam, of the Emerald Queen," he said.

He was small in stature, perhaps a shade shorter than Lucy, who was used to having everyone tower over her. His beard and hair were a bristling black, combed and well-groomed. His skin was leathery and bronzed and his eyes were a perilous poet's green. When he flexed his hands impatiently, she noted their well-kept nails and the bright red stone framed in gold on his left hand. His clothes were gaudy although wrinkled and not much washed.

"Well?"

"I don't know why I'm here."

He frowned. "Let me cut right to the bone, lad. I will not put up with prevarication and the tongue twisting that wizards are known for." He nodded down at the bundle of burlap and legs. "What's that then, my fine fellows?"

"Tried to stop us from nicking her...er, him," one said. He jerked the sack away and a pale, freckle-faced boy blinked upwards from the floor. "Figgered we always needed canaries."

There was a knock on the door. "Cap'n, 'at finger-wiggler ya wanted tah speak to is 'ere."

"Throw them both in the hold for now," Captain Miryam said. "Give him a taste of what no cooperation would be like." He smiled faintly at Lucy. "Not that your present form isn't charming enough, but you might consider releasing it."

"Put them in cold iron chains," he said to the men. "Keep the candles I gave you burning in there, that'll keep him woozy enough to cast no spells. Check on them every turn of the glass."

They were hauled away.

***

The hold, Lucy found, was deep in the ship's belly, damp and cold. The timbers creaked and groaned around them and every time a wave slammed into the ship, Lucy felt the blow through the wall to which she had been chained. The older of the two sailors brought out a fat black candle and stooped to set it in a brass holder bolted to the floor. The younger stood staring at Lucy. He was a scrawny, scowling boy, his head shaved to gray-brown fuzz.

The other was old enough to be his grandfather. After setting the wick a-kindle, he took the boy by the shoulder with an admonitory shake and jerked him from the room.

The door slammed behind them and there was a clunk as it was barred. Lucy raised her head to look across at her companion.

He was pale and jug-eared in the flickering candle light, although a thatch of red hair hid part of the mushroom-white flaps set along his head. Freckles splattered across his cheekbones. His eyes were the color of Lucy's, a watery blue.

In turn, he saw a small, blond girl, dressed in a neatly patched cloak. Her face was narrow and triangular, and her mouth was rosebud prim, though not as pretty as that phrase implies.

"Well," he said. "Here we are, I guess."

"Who are you?"

"My name's Devon."

"Lucy."

"Pleased to make your acquaintance." His tone was cordial and she wondered at the power of manners that could somehow provide a script for this dreadful, chaotic situation.

"What are we doing here?"

"As far as I can tell," Devon said. "The pirates thought they were kidnapping someone from the College of Mages and got you instead. I was behind a ways and saw you getting grabbed, so I ran after you and was snatched in turn. I'm here to be a canary, whatever that is. There you have my knowledge's sum and total."

"Why did they think I'm a man, though?"

"Mages can go about in many disguises," Devon said. "Some actually change their shapes, while others rely on glamourie, illusion-casting.

Lots like to walk around town that way so they're not spotted as mages. Everyone assumes mages can conjure gold and they jack up the prices like you wouldn't believe."

"How do you know so much about it?"

"I'm also a student of the College of Mages."

"Are you the person they were looking for?"

"Oh, no," he said hurriedly. "No, I'm not. But listen, I'm thinking that if they think you're him, that's the only thing keeping you from being used as a canary. And while I don't know what being a canary means, I'm willing to bet that since they have to kidnap people to be them, it's not a great thing."

Lucy mulled this over. "You're probably right."

"You can at least find out what they want," Devon said.

"What if he asks me to drop the disguise again?"

"Tell him it was a shape shifting spell that went awry and you were heading back to the College to have a Master Mage remove it. That happens all the time."

"It does?"

"You'd be surprised how often."

"I can't do it," she said, turning back to the question. "He'll glare at me and I'll start crying."

He frowned over at her. "Just put your chin up," he said. "Think about him naked."

She blushed, even more frightened. She still couldn't figure out how she, Lucy the Mouse, had ended up on a boat with pirates. It was like something from a ballad but much less glamorous somehow. She hadn't realized how frightening adventures could be.

They heard footsteps and the door being unbarred. The younger pirate stuck his head in and looked between them, then at the candle. Before either could react, he withdrew his head with a rapid snakelike motion and slammed the door.

"Not much chance for conversation," Devon said.

"How long do you think they'll keep us here?"

"Your guess is as good as mine. Look, Lucy, you've got to bluff your way through this. Pretend you're someone else. Perhaps some character from a play you've seen?"

"I haven't seen any plays since I was very little," she said, dismayed.

"Well, what about one that you liked as a child?"

She thought. She remembered the stories that she loved listening to. In the bedroom, all four children crouched around her mother's skirts. Lucy had been so small she could barely remember the stories, but they came back to her now: The Rabbit that Stole the Moon, and Mary Silverhands and Sister Wind and the Golden Bridle, Whitepetal and Blackleaf, and the Princess with the Copper Scales.

There had been a street puppet theater, a cloth screen stretched over a wooden framework, so different on one side from the other. In front, the puppets moved, but past the curtains had been the dancing puppeteers, pitching their voices upward, avoiding each other as they maneuvered the wooden sticks manipulating the forms above them.

She remembered Mary Silverhands, her glowing hands held before her, turning everything she touched to metal: the food on her plate, the drink in her glass. And the blonde-haired puppet's dignity, its upright stance, the patient grace conveyed by its inanimate face.

She closed her eyes and envisioned herself something other than Lucy, the youngest, the clumsiest, the least listened to and the most overlooked. She was Mary, her life a constant struggle to look out for those around her, to avoid unleashing the deadly power that would, unless contained, turn the whole world to silver.

"All right," she said. It was Mary's voice, not a quaver, not a quiver.

"You'll do it?"

"Yes," Mary said.

***

The young pirate poked his head in twice more before she was bundled back into the Captain's cabin. Another black candle guttered in the corner. She couldn't tell much difference between the air outside and the candle smoke, but she was so weary by now that everything seemed unreal and brighter than life to her, like a hallucinatory fever-dream.

"Well?" the Captain demanded.

"What did you want with me?"

"Are you the Pot King's son?"

"Maybe..." she stammered.

He leaned forward to stare into her eyes.

"Yes or no!" She flinched back from his shout. Her mouth worked noiselessly, terror taking her tongue.

"Bring the other in and cut his throat to show this one we mean business," he said to the pirate holding her.

"Aye, sir."

Mary, she thought, I'm Mary. If I reached out to touch this man, he would be dead in an instant. "No!" she managed to squeak. Her voice was barely audible.

He slouched back in his chair, looking pleased, but did not speak.

She gasped, fighting to shape the words. "Please, you mustn't!"

The door opened again and the pirate stood there, holding Devon against his chest, a wicked silver line against the boy's throat.

"I am, I'll do it, please don't!" she shrieked. The Captain held up a forefinger to the pirate holding Devon. The knife stayed where it was.

"I'm his son, I am, I'll help you however you like," she babbled.

"Clearly the canary is of more use here than stowed away elsewhere," the Captain said. He stroked his beard, eying them. "Do you intend to take your true form, Prince Nikolai?"

She pulled herself up out of her panic, clinging to the thought of Mary. What was the story Devon had provided? "I can't. The magic went awry. I need another mage to lift it. A Master Mage."

His eyes narrowed. "I see. Pity we didn't keep the sorcerer around longer. I congratulate you on your ingenuity. Who would think such a trifling form would mask a budding mage?"

"Trifling?"

"We have no use for you until we reach the Coral Tower. But I'm presuming you would rather see the sky and sun than spend the entire journey in the hold?"

Lucy frowned at him.

"All that I require," he said. "Is your word on your name. The vow that no wizard can break without losing his or her magic."

The frown stayed on her face, knitting her translucent brows together.

"And you," he said to Devon, who still dangled, his chin stretched upward to avoid the blade. "You'll swear to make no attempts at escape either."

"How could I escape?" Devon said. "Jump overboard and walk away on the water?"

"Just do it!"

They repeated the words after the Captain.

"When do we set sail?" Lucy asked. Perhaps there might be way to get word to her family if she was allowed on deck.

The Captain laughed.

"When?" he said. "Two hours ago, that's when. We're far out to sea by now."

"Where are we headed?" Devon asked.

The Captain pointed at Lucy. "Her...I mean his father's spawning grounds, the Lesser Southern Isles."

He looked to the other pirates. "Take them away for now."

***

They were fed, although it was a dried fish, some hard biscuit and a half mug of sour watery beer apiece.

"The Lesser Southern Isles will take us two weeks to reach," Devon said.

"How do you know? Are you from there?"

"They teach us geography – that's maps and how to read them – in the College." He stared forward, thinking. "Magic is unpredictable in the Lesser Southern Isles. There are artifacts there from other ages, like the Coral Tower and the Speaking Skull. They say anything can happen in the Lesser Southern Isles, that gods are born and remade there. I guess we'll see."

Lucy sighed. "Two weeks."

"Will your family miss you?" Devon asked. Back in the echoing hold, Lucy wondered how she had not understood the departure sounds, the heavy timbers' creak and sway and the distant shouts and clatter of footsteps.

"Two weeks," she repeated. "No, they won't. Well, yes, they'll miss me, perhaps, but they'll have no idea where to look."

"I am sure that the College will set seeking spells after me," he said. "It's just a matter of holding out until this ship stops and the spells have a chance to catch up."

"You're a wizard – can you send word back about where we're headed?"

"Not without violating my oath and jeopardizing my magic's source."

"What would happen if you broke your word?"

He looked away.

***

In the morning, they were allowed to stroll the deck. Lucy would have liked to lean on Devon's arm but as the supposed Pot-King's son she felt it necessary to exhibit a masculine swagger. She hoped it was more convincing than it felt.

They exchanged histories. Devon had grown up in the Old Islands, magic-wracked lands populated by scattered tribes. The Pot-King, he said, struggled to recruit as many as he could.

"Everyone says they know the secret of his power and everyone says something different," he said. "But he's a match for any three sorcerers on the Old Continent."

"Then why isn't his son a powerful wizard?" Lucy said.

"Mages don't manifest power until they start to come of age," he said. "You know, when they start getting beards." He blushed and left the rest unsaid: his squeaky voice and downy cheek showed no trace of manhood.

Lucy told him about being the youngest, an unexpected and unwanted child trailing after her louder, bolder, braver siblings.

"Mouse," she said. "And Meepling, and Slink, and Little Miss Silent, that's what they call me."

"I have no brothers and sisters to call me anything," Devon said. "I envy you."

***

As they approached to the Lesser Southern Isles, the days and nights grew balmier. The cook taught them how to fish and how to throw a weighted hand-net to catch the schools of small fish or shrimp swimming in the wave tops. Whatever they caught showed up in their evening bread and fish stew.

After dinner they were allowed to listen to the stories of the sailors, who sat passing tobacco pipes, telling tales of kraken and merfolk and great living islands that dove when unwary sailors went ashore and built fires to cook their meals.

Captain Miryam did not take part in the storytelling. Lucy saw him rarely—a glimpse now and again as he paced the front deck, green eyes gleaming in the evening shadows.

***

Two days later, the Captain sent for Lucy again. He unrolled a map and gestured at her to look.

What she presumed were the Lesser Southern Isles spread across the parchment in coin-shaped irregularities. One blob that aspired to hand-sized sat towards the map's upper edge. The Captain tapped the space beside it.

"This," he said. "is where we are now."

He pointed to a circle halfway down the map. "And here is the Coral Tower."

"Which is?" Lucy asked.

He snorted. "Your daddy keeps it all close, eh, son?" He stroked his moustache, eying Lucy. "Or are you playing it coy so I'll underestimate you?" He smiled. "I presume you know the perils of a young girl caught on a pirate ship. They may be all charm and fishing lore while you're under my wing, but should that...protection be withdrawn, you would find your form more disadvantageous."

"I told you, I can't lift the spell," Lucy said.

He studied her. "Very well. The Coral Tower is an ancient artifact, discovered when these Isles were first settled. It sits in the water, surrounded by coral reefs. Inside, a staircase leads down. Some say to the Earth's center, others to chambers filled with treasure."

He shrugged. "What I know is that your father went down there and returned with immense power, and that he had to use his own blood to pay for that bargain. Now the tower is sealed to all but those of that blood – you'll lead the way and take me down to where I can make my own deal."

"Oh," Lucy said blankly. "All right."

He smiled tightly at her. This close in the cabin, she could smell him, sweat and the sweet amber fragrance that came from the clothes chest at the foot of the uncomfortably close and lavish bed. She felt hyper-aware of his presence, the smell of the anise seeds he chewed, the way his moustache curled, the fine wrinkles at the corners of his electric green eyes.

"All right," he said. He sighed, staying where he was. "What use are you, little mage?" His hand took her shoulder; it was warm through her shirt's worn linen. She shivered. Something coiled and uncoiled in her core.

"What are you like under this disguise?" Captain Miryam's voice was husky and soft. "Is this the form you yearn for, the form of your soul itself? Are you a demure little maiden, eyelashes so blonde and fine I can barely see them in the lamplight?" His breath stirred the hairs on her neck. She gasped for breath, a sudden shocked sound that made him withdraw.

Her face burned as she was taken back to the hold.

***

The days and nights grew warmer yet. On a sky blue afternoon, gulls wheeling above like lookouts, they glimpsed the Coral Tower.

It was much larger than Lucy had imagined. In her head it had been the size of her home, three rooms, grown up and downward into a long thin stalk. In reality, it seemed as wide around as a small city and she understood now the awed undertone with which both Devon and the Captain had named it. It was round and windows spanned its circumference, each large enough for their ship to pass through. The lines of windows continued upward, upward, towards a top that was far above in the blueness. Its color was a rosy, warm shade, but bird droppings encrusted the lower levels, thick mottled gray and white layers.

"It's at its best right after a storm," Devon said. "Then everything is washed clean, and you can see all the details." He stared forward at the tower, eyes wide.

The Captain came up behind them. "We'll be pulling in tonight," he said. "You'll do your part, lad, or else your young friend here will die."

Not for the first time, Lucy regretted her disguise's complications.

The pirates dissented when it came time to brave the Coral Tower. Most stayed on board. They tied the ship to a railing near a set of steps a dozen horses wide, stretching upward into the tower. Two sailors shimmied down to anchor the rope ladder that most used, but Lucy and Devon were both lowered, arms tied to their sides.

"According to the sorcerer, it'll take a while for the Tower to know you," the Captain said to Lucy. "We'll stay here tonight."

They climbed the stairs, which were slippery, overgrown with wet yellow weed ribbed with shadowy purple. At the entrance they paused, gazing inward. There was no interior to the Tower, just a vast upward stretch. A narrow, unrailed staircase spiraled along the inside, leading upwards. They headed into the middle, where a black pit marked where a similar staircase led down into the earth.

The sailors built a fire of scavenged driftwood beside the pit. A small pot set amid the flames boiled with merry abandon, smelling of boiled double-fin and onions.

A sailor came from the ship, bringing a narrow wooden chest to the Captain. Opening it, he took out silken bands, each mounted with a slippery gray soapstone disk. He passed them out to everyone except Devon and Lucy, but tied one on her. Like the rest, he wore his fastened around his head, the stone disk resting flat against his forehead.

"I have been exploring and researching this Tower for over a decade," he said. "While many chambers will not open except to the Pot King's blood, since he was the last person to bind energies here, there are others that can be explored. Many hold sorcerous energies that play upon one's spirit – these disks absorb the effulgences but can hold only so much. So to find these pools of invisible, noxious influences, we use captives, just as miners use canaries in coal mines to signal deadly gas. Should you," he nodded towards Devon. "fall prey to the energies and seek to destroy yourself, we will know we are in the presence of such, and hurry on."

"That is the usual sign?" Devon asked.

"A few have managed to hurl themselves into the pit that lies at the center and fall for we do not know how long."

Lucy shivered.

"There is no need to expose her to all this," Devon said.

"Who?"

He pointed at Lucy with his chin. "I'm the Pot-King's son. She's an innocent who got swept up in your plot unawares."

The Captain frowned, looking between them. "We'll take both and see who falls prey to the energies first," he said, removing Lucy's disk. "A sorcerer will have enough training to overcome the worst effects."

They slept there that night, although Lucy did not feel that she slept at all. The inside of the tower roared with the waves' murmur, magnifying it into a steady throbbing at the back of her head. She strained her ears, listening for noises from the depths of the hole. Devon was restless too. In the early hours she was roused by clamor. His restless thrashings had knocked a supply pack over the side. The Captain swore at him, but kept his voice down.

I can't do this anymore, Lucy thought, filled with despair at the anger in his words. I can't get up in the morning and go down into that pit. Tears leaked from her eyes, and a shudder passed through her as the waves cried out again.

There's no choice, she realized. They won't listen to my refusals. It's not like escaping a school day by claiming stomach ache. Mary Silverhands had no choice, she simply endured and did the best she could.

***

In the morning, they started down: Lucy, Devon, the Captain, and two sailors, the two who had originally caught them, Ned and Pete. Ned was the bluff-faced, stocky older man, and Pete the younger. They were all roped together as they proceeded down the stairway: a sailor, then Devon, then Lucy, then the other sailor, then the Captain. The walls were unadorned and slick with salty moisture.

The nightmarish, narrow part seemed to continue for hours but eventually they came to a place where tunnels led off in every direction, allowing them to make camp and sleep. The Captain told Devon that he might explore. The boy took a torch and headed into the darkness. His pace was quick and eager, untired where the rest ached with weariness.

A rope trailed after the Captain and back up towards the top. It led to a small windlass that had been set up beside the hole with sailors to watch over it.

"We may be a while down here," he explained to Lucy. She sat a few feet away from the pit's edge, watching the darkness while the sailors built a fire and set water boiling for tea. "And it will be easier to have them lower supplies than have someone go fetching and carrying along the staircase."

"We might be down here for days?" Lucy asked, dismayed. The oppressive darkness dampened her spirits.

"In two more circles of the rim, we will have come as deep as I ever have. There is a closed doorway that I think will open to the Pot King's blood. But who knows what lies beyond it, or how long it will take to wrestle the magic free?" He laughed. "Perhaps when all is said and done, we'll come flying up out of the pit, hovering on great wings like falcons before we burst out across the Isles in glory and splendor."

Lucy continued to watch the darkness.

"So you are not the Pot King's son?" he asked.

She shook her head. "Just a girl," she said.

"Ah," he said. "Just a girl."

The silence stretched out between them.

"Do you know why going into the earth's heart is so perilous?" he asked.

"Why?"

"Down there, we are closer to the bones of sorcery. Emotions go awry and thoughts can damage you. So it is best to be calm down here, to avoid emotional extremes." His voice was strained. "Satisfying lust, for one."

"Oh," she said. And then, "Oh!"

He stooped to whisper, "But when we are back on the surface, just a girl, we will speak of this again." He turned and went to oversee the sailors as they prepared the meal.

I am not invisible to him, she thought. Back home she was used to her sisters drawing men's stares, used to their gaze passing over her absently. But Jusef Miryam's green eyes saw her, every inch of her. She smiled to herself.

***

Half a day later, they stood before the portal. The rope had been fastened beside their camp at the pit's edge and they had paused to eat and drink before entering the tunnels and coming to the small, boxy room, two doors set along its northern wall.

"See?" Captain Miryam said, looking pleased. "That door and that both were closed before. We'll try the right hand side first."

They wove through roseate stone tunnels, lighting their way with fish-oil lanterns that sent out a black, stink-laden smoke. By now, she thought, they were miles below the ocean's surface. Sometimes there were signs of earlier visitors – writing scratched or painted or in one case seared into the stone, nothing that Lucy could read.

The tunnel ended in a door made of a different material, a pearly slab that reflected the lanterns' sullen glow. The Captain gestured to Devon, who jittered in place, impatient. "After you, lad."

Drawn in their wake and trailed by the sailors, Lucy entered the room. It had a sea-shell's inner glow and was far wider within than it had seemed from without. An immense ribbed ceiling stretched overhead, and white crystal veins laced like ivy across the pink surface.

"Captain Miryam," Devon said. "If you allow me to step forward and seize the same power as my father, I will take you to safety. Otherwise I will watch as you, a novice untutored in these arts, are consumed by its energies and then step forward and take the same power as my father."

His voice was altered, taking on an older, bitterer cadence but still high and excited. Lucy stared at him.

"Who are you?" she said.

"It's his son still," Captain Miryam said. He sounded amused. "So the rumors are true – he keeps you barred from adolescence and has for decades, to prevent you from challenging him."

Devon's face worked angrily. "Yes!" he spat. "Decades I've been a boy, decades I've been in this form, puny child not fit for adult company. But now I can have the power, and mature my body after all."

Lucy paid them no attention. She stepped forward, seeking the glow's source. Here in this oddly shaped chamber, the acoustics were erratic. She heard whispers in her ears, half-heard tugs at her attention.

The Captain turned to the sailors. "Hold him," he said.

The sailors stepped forward to vanish in showers of bloody sparks. Devon's thin lips crept up from his teeth to assume an eerie rictus.

You have to hurry, Mary's voice said to Lucy. She turned back – surely she was close, so close to the source of the light. She managed somehow to turn a corner while standing still, and the light was all around her, seeping into her bones.

I'm Mary Silverhands now, she thought, distracted by the power washing through her. Someone was shouting, Devon was shouting, shouting at her, and she put out a hand and recoiled in horror as her energy and his met and marred each other.

She watched as Devon fell away into pieces, as he was unmade by the collision of the light. Sorrowfully, she kept her own edges from raveling, rewove them. The energy roiled through her, wore her like a wave, but she closed her eyes and focused, drew her awareness down into a single point, and relaxed and opened them. She stood in the chamber, alone except for Jusef, who stood staring at her. Char marks were laid upon the wall to mark the sailors' passing. There was no sign of Devon.

She led the way back to the camp. He followed her in silence. She walked feeling the energy leak from her, feeling it collide with the world. It was a constant struggle to keep from changing it, to keep from doing things like letting wildflowers spring up in her wake, or the air in her lungs be breathed out as lastflower perfume.

At the camp and the pit's edge, she paused.

He took her hand, level-eyed. She leaned to touch her lips to his and this time she did give into the urge. With her kiss, he breathed in sweetness: the air in a pear orchard just as the first sunshine touches the blossoms open. He rocked back on his heels with the magic's passionate force, his green eyes wild and entreating.

She unfolded great falcon wings and leaped into the pit, flying upwards towards the dot of light so far above. He fell to his knees and watched, watched as a new goddess ascended towards the skies of the Lesser Southern Isles.

CHAPTER 9
SCENE

What it is

A scene is usually a moment in time that has come to you. It usually has strong visual elements, and something is usually happening, such as a battle, or has just happened in it (a battlefield after the fighting is done). It is probably something that would appear at a significant moment of a story and not be peripheral to it.

What it provides

Everything but the plot. But actually, that's not true. What is the main source of tension in the scene, what is the conflict that is driving things? That is probably a version of the overall plot.

A scene gives you a strong slice of the world and all that is implicit in that, including history and culture.

If characters are included in your scene, they are usually doing or have just done something more purposeful than just milling about. You have some sense of their occupation, their economic circumstances, and often some nuances of their relationship.

Considerations

Why would this scene matter? As noted earlier, it's something that is significant to the story. Does it appear near the beginning and spark things into motion, or does it appear at the end and sum the action of the story up

What are the circumstances behind the scene? If it's a visual splendor, there is some usually technology or magic underlying it and creating it.

What is the context in which it's being viewed?

What is striking about the image to you and how can you best convey that to a reader?

Pitfalls

Is your scene just some sort of natural vista? That's going to be hard to develop something from. In that case, think about what might make that vista unusual or unexpected.

Make it more than just a pretty picture. Something has to happen in a story and moments where there is just description slow narrative down drastically. If the camera is lingering on something, make it something riveting. Use interesting and lively verbs as well as paying attention to sentence length and paragraphing in order to counteract the slowing of the motion.

Next steps

Consider the viewpoint. Who is seeing the scene? What is their relationship to it? What do they know about it and what questions do they have about it?

Write the accompanying dialogue. What's being said in the scene, and why does it matter? Who is speaking and why?

The moment may be brief or extended; generally the longer it lasts, the more it gives you. Think about what happens immediately before and after the scene that you have; should some of that be included in the story?

Exercises

1. Sometimes it's helpful to expand the idea of the visual. How might you convey this scene in a graphic novel? Write it out as though it were a script. OA: Write the entire story this way.
2. Describe same scene with two different moods, preferably ones as different from each other as they can be, such as a joyous description of the scene versus a saddened or enraged one. OA: Expand to 3-4 moods and/or combine several moods in a single description.
3. Construct a mirror scene, a second scene in which many elements of the first are repeated, but different actions take place. OA: Figure out where in the story your scene takes place and put your scene in a spot that would balance it in the story. For example, if your story is at the beginning, create one at the end, or vice versa. (If it falls in the middle, create something at either the beginning or end, but contemplate making the task even more complicated by doing both.)

Case study: (Magnificent Pigs)

For me the story "Magnificent Pigs" began with an image of its final scene, with the pigs flying away bearing Jilly's bed into the night. Once I had that, I knew she was important, but also that she was not the protagonist. That would be whoever was watching her fly away into the night, which turned out to be her brother.

"Magnificent Pigs" is a good example of how, once you have a scene, you can begin to accrete things. I had read about a recent art project that involved tattooing pigs; this became the way that they acquire their wings. A trip to the tattoo parlor with my friend Kris, who was getting a tattoo, lent some details for verisimilitude, and she told me the story about her mother telling her Charlotte was always alive in the book in order to console her (and gave me permission to use it in the story). To me, that's a lovely little note, because of course it has a parallel—Jilly will also always be alive in the story.

Magnificent Pigs

The spring before it happened, I went upstairs and found my ten year old sister Jilly crying. Charlotte's Web, which we'd been reading together at bedtime all that week, lay splayed on the floor where she'd thrown it.

"What's wrong?" I said, hovering in the doorway. As Jilly had gotten sicker I tried to offer her the illusion of her own space but remained ready in case big brotherly comfort was needed.

"I was reading ahead because I liked it so much--and Charlotte dies!" she managed to gasp between sobs.

The big brass bed creaked in protest as I sat down beside her. Gathering her into my arms, I rocked her back and forth. It was well past sunset and the full-faced moon washed into the room, spilling across the blue rag rug like milk and gleaming on the bed knobs so they looked like balls of icy light contending with the dim illumination of Jilly's bedside lamp.

"It's a book, Jilly, just a book," I said.

She shook her head, cheeks blotched red and wet with tears.

"But, Aaron, Charlotte's dead!" she choked out again.

I retrieved the book from the middle of the room and set it in front of her. "Look," I said. "If we open the book up again at the beginning, Charlotte's alive. She'll always be alive in the book."

Sobs quieted to hiccups as she reached for the book, looking dubious. When she opened it to the first chapter, I began to read. "' Where's Papa going with that ax?' said Fern to her mother as they were setting the table for breakfast. 'Out to the hoghouse,' replied Mrs. Arable. 'Some pigs were born last night.'"

Curling against me, she let me read the first two chapters. After she slipped away to sleep, I tucked the blanket around her then went downstairs to cry my own tears.

***

My father and mother were farmers. They were raised by farmers who had themselves been raised by farmers and so on back to Biblical days. They saw my talent for drawing as a hobby until the age of seventeen, when I proposed that my major in college be an uneasy mixture of art and agriculture. They were dubious but they were also good-natured sorts who only wanted the best for me. So they sent me, eldest of their two children, off to Indiana University. Jilly takes after them.

Jilly, a late arrival to the family, was six years old at the point I left and consumed most of their attention, which I did not begrudge her. From day one she was a tiny, perfect addition to our household and I loved her.

Three years later on a rainy September afternoon my parents died in a car accident and I returned home to the farm to take care of Jilly. A few townfolk felt I shouldn't be allowed to raise her by myself but when I hit twenty one a year later, that magic number at which you apparently become an adult, they stopped fussing.

Since the other driver was not only drunk but driving a bus with faulty brakes that another company had failed to fix, the court settlement provided enough to live on. It wasn't a lot but I supplemented it by raising pigs and apples in the way my parents always had and taking them to Indianapolis where the pigs were purchased by a plant that makes organic bacon, pork, and sausage and the apples by a cider mill. I didn't mind the farm work. I'd get up in the morning, take care of things, and find myself a few hours in the afternoon to work in the studio I'd fixed myself in the attic

A year ago Jilly started getting stomachaches so bad they had her doubled over and crying. When I first took her to the hospital, they diagnosed it as Crohn's disease. Six months later, after I'd learned the vocabulary of aminosalicylates and corticosteroids and immunomodulators, they switched to a simpler word: cancer.

Insurance covered the medical bills. It didn't cover much else so I laid aside my art and bought some more pigs. I had to hire a nurse to take care of Jilly whenever I couldn't – I wanted someone with her all the time. I didn't want her lonely or unable to help herself.

At first I hired a chilly but competent woman, Miss Andersen. She was expensive, but I figured she was worth it. I had a crazy idea that I'd use my talent to become a tattoo artist and make enough extra cash to pay her. A Superior mobile tattoo set from E-Bay cost me a hundred bucks and got me started. I named my enterprise Magnificent Pigs, in honor of Wilbur.

But tattoos aren't a high demand item in Traversville, and you need to practice a lot to get any good at it. Once I'd run out of old high school friends who were willing to let me work on them in the name of a free tattoo, I turned to the pigs.

It's not as cruel as it sounds, I swear. According to the vet pig skin is tough as nails and has few nerve endings. He sells me cartons of a topical anesthetic lotion that I use beforehand, just in case.

And the pigs have never objected. They're placid beasts – give them a bowl of mash and they don't care what you do. My dad believed in playing classical music to calm the animals so I crank Beethoven cello suites to hide the buzz of the needle, and go to town. The first time I took a tattooed pig to the slaughterhouse, they gave me odd looks when they saw where I'd inscribed "Mother," "Semper Fi," and "Tattooing gets pretty boring after a while" in blue and red and black on the leathery white skin, but as long as it didn't mark the meat, it was okay.

I didn't achieve my dreams of becoming a brand name tattoo artist, no matter how many coiling koi and serpents I covered the pigs with. Southern Indiana is a conservative place –the KKK had its second rebirth nearby—and there is no room for much outside the mainstream designs like scorpions, the Confederate flag, and tribal designs from no tribe that ever existed. I liked the business because it made me feel like an artist but few people came out for tattoos.

I had to let Miss Andersen go, promising I'd have her back wages for her within six months. She wasn't happy about it but had a good contract with the nursing home waiting so she let it slide. Jilly was glad to see her depart but didn't tell me till weeks later about the meanness that had revealed itself when tending a hapless ten year old.

"She was just mean," Jilly said.

"She never touched you, did she?" I asked cautiously.

"No, not like that. She pinched me a few times but mostly she said mean things. Like what a shame it was that I was an orphan and how you'd probably get rid of me when you got married."

I looked at her but her face was clear and unworried.

"That didn't bother you, Jilly?" I asked.

"I knew you'll always take care of me."

Which was all fine and well but even so Miss Andersen's departure made it feel as though things were pressing in on all sides. Nightmares lapped at my sleep all that night.

The next day, strung out on caffeine and weariness, I stood in the cramped grocery store aisle looking at jams and sandwich spreads and couldn't decide between crunchy and smooth peanut butter. I literally couldn't remember which Jilly or I preferred. I must have stood there for ten minutes.

See, one of the side effects of the disease is nausea and loss of appetite. Peanut butter's one of the few things Jilly will eat, and it's high in protein. So it's important to bring home the right one.

There's a wide variety of peanut butter labels. I stood there, looking at Jif and Skippy and Peter Pan and Kroger brand, going through the same loop in my head over and over: "No I think I like crunchy and Jilly likes smooth, but maybe it's the other way around, and what other groceries do we need, but first – crunchy or smooth?" While this frenzied loop continued, I became aware that a woman and her cart had been circling me, going back and forth in the aisle and warding off other shoppers. The Muzak on the store intercom switched from one piano piece to another.

Finally she stopped beside me. "Buy them both," she advised, and it broke the spell that had held me.

I turned. She was an elderly woman dressed in black, a blue and white scarf bound around her hair to hold it in place. She had an enormous beaklike nose and bright black eyes that glittered at me as though daring me to rebuff her. It was Mrs. Huber, whose husband had died a few years before. I don't know why she stuck in Bedford. She had, and was an object of some curiosity, being the town's only Jew. Jilly and I are a step outside that, being people whose parents were born elsewhere as well as the family of the town invalid.

"Thank you," I said, and took down two jars. She stood beside me, and it didn't feel awkward at all. Like we were family who had happened to meet there and would see each other again at dinner.

She said, "The little girl needs a nurse, no?"

"Yeah, she does." I said. I gestured at the shelves. "It's okay, though. I just got a little side-tracked, that's all."

We stared at each other. My only other encounter with Mrs. Huber had been selling her salt water taffy when I was in sixth grade and trying to win a trip to Washington, D.C. in the school candy drive. I found out later she bought candy from every kid that approached her. With three grades selling, ten to fifteen kids in each class, that must have been a substantial pile of sweets.

She didn't look too much older now. The lines around her eyes were more defined and her lips drooped at a harsher angle. Finally she said, simply, "You need nurse too maybe?" and after that we came to an arrangement.

Jilly loved her like a mother. I got fond of her myself. There was a certain irony to a Jew living on a pig farm, particularly with a tattoo artist. She didn't keep kosher, so she ate with us each night, although she'd never touch pork. I cooked any pork chops, or sausage, or bacon, or other variants of pig meat. But most of the time I left it to her to cook. She coaxed Jilly's tender appetite with blintzes and rugelach, kugel and kreplach. The kitchen took on a simmer of cinnamon that was a pleasant change from TV dinners.

After supper we'd sit in the parlor, Jilly watching TV or reading while I studied up on farming or tattooing methods and Mrs. H. knitted. She turned out shawls, scarves, baby blankets, and a multitude of sweaters for Jilly, with patterns of pigs or flowers. Jilly's favorite was the one with her name knitted into the front. She'd scold me for working too hard and when I came in bone weary from a day of fretting about pig vaccines or Jilly's latest set of tests, she'd say in her harsh accent, "Worries go down better with soup."

Sometimes I thought that God had sent her by way of apology.

I don't want to make it sound like everything was fine. But it wasn't as bad as it could be, at least for a while.

I was practicing on one of the pigs, writing out words, when Jilly came into the barn and leaned on the bench near me. It was early spring warm. By now we were long past recognizing the smell of pig shit – sometimes I forgot that it clung like an invisible film to my clothing until I noticed people edging away from me in lines.

The other smells weren't hidden by the omnipresent odor: the sour redolence of corn mash, the fresh tang of the straw underfoot, the distant sweetness of apple blossom coming in through the window.

"What are you doing?" Jilly asked.

"Practicing writing words," I said.

"What's that?" she said, pointing to a passage of text on the pig's rounded back.

"It's the first verse of 'Stairway to Heaven.'"

"Nice."

"It was the only poetry I could remember off the top of my head," I said.

She sat there watching me, so I started tattooing the words that Charlotte uses to describe Wilbur onto the pig's broad back. When I reached "Magnificent", she giggled, just as Mrs. H. called us to dinner. She went ahead while I cleaned off my needles.

She asked me at dinner, "Don't we have runts that we could keep? Like Wilbur?"

"Jilly, we can't afford to keep them as pets," I said. She couldn't have a cat or dog because of allergies, not to mention my own fears about compromising her immune system. She started to protest and I cut her off. "That's final."

But that night, after Jilly was asleep, Mrs. H. said to me, "Maybe you should give her pig for a pet."

"We can't afford it."

She looked at me, her eyes sad. "I think she might be gone before the pig get sent off."

"She's getting better," I said. "Look at how she chattered all through dinner."

But she was right, and we both knew it.

"When one must, one can," she said gently.

***

The next morning dawned hard and bright, and it seemed inevitable that after a long night's birthing, one of the pregnant sows had six perfect piglets surrounding her in the straw. I took Jilly out to look at them and told her to pick one.

"It has to be the runt," she said. And then, "But they're all the same size!"

I looked at her, leaning on the railing with her gawky bird-like arms, so thin that she could wear rubber bands for bracelets, and felt a hard lump in my throat.

"Take them all, Jilly," I said. "They'll all be your pigs."

***

She named them Celeste, Patience, Rutabaga, Bill, Princess Ozma, and (predictably) Wilbur. Mrs. H. professed to hate them. "Trafe!" she said, and spat whenever they were mentioned, but I noticed her assembling leftovers for Jilly to feed them.

Jilly spent hours by the pen, wrapped in a blanket and watching the piglets with an expression of beatific joy. They came to know her and would come when she called. She spent enough time petting them that I got in the habit of spraying them down with a hose in the mornings and evenings, to cut down on the amount of pig smell that ended up clinging to her. The mother pig remained unmoved by Jilly's appreciation of her young, but when the piglets were napping, piled on each other like puppies, tiny tails swishing like sporadic windshield wipers, she and Jilly beamed down at them with identical expressions.

The piglets grew fast, prancing around the yard like models in high heels, stealing bits of food from Jilly's hand . . . and all the while my baby sister diminished, curled in on herself as though she were becoming a little old woman, as though each day the cancer claimed another morsel of her frail form, making her lighter and lighter. At some point soon, it would win and take her away.

***

Jilly's pigs were fat and fine, sleek as colts and almost full grown when I came home one day to find her weeping even harder than she had for Charlotte, while Mrs. H. fussed around her.

"What happened?" I demanded. "Is she in pain?"

"That very bad woman," Mrs. H. said. "She came by to speak to you, Mr. Aaron, about her money. Such a tongue in her head should rot."

"What did she say?"

"It was Miss Andersen. I told her that I was going to school next year," Jilly said. She clung to me, and hot tears soaked my neck. "Because by then I would be better, and she laughed and said I'd be better when pigs grow wings and fly. Is it true, Aaron? Am I not going to get better? Am I going to die?"

"No, no," I said, clutching her to me. "No, Jilly, you are going to school next year."

Mrs. H. regarded me. We'd had this argument before. She thought I should tell Jilly, but I wouldn't. I wouldn't let her know she was dying. That would make it too real.

"No," I said, and pressed a kiss onto the top of her head. "It's all right, Jilly. It will be all right."

She let herself be comforted, but all through that evening, I felt myself angrier and angrier at Miss Andersen's words. Going outside, I looked at Jilly's pigs. Fat and happy, while my sister lay inside wasting away.

I went inside and fetched my tattoo kit. I was tired, but too angry to sleep, and I could tell I'd be up for hours. Mrs. H. came out and waved goodbye to me as she revved her tiny Civic and drove away, her headlights cutting swaths in the darkness of the farm road. Overhead, the stars were bright and distinct in the fathomless sky. I opened the door to the pen and Jilly's tame pigs followed me into the barn.

I set up shop in an abandoned stall, and when I was finished with one pig, it would walk out to the others to be inspected proprietarily while another one came in.

I gave them wings.

It was the finest work I'd ever done. For Celeste, there were a phoenix's wings, flame bright,coiling red and yellow. Patience's skin displayed a dove's wings, muted in color, browns and grays that showed like bruises against the white hide. A blue jay's wings for Rutabaga, a vivid iridescent blue striped with black. Bill got green plumage like a parrot's, touched with scarlet and indigo at the tips. Princess Ozma's were gold and silver, a metallic sheen that reflected light and cast it across the pen. And Wilbur had black wings, black as night. Black as death.

It took hours as they stood patiently beneath the buzzing needle, letting me etch the lines into their skin, wiping away the blood that welled up beneath the images. And when I was done, I was so tired I could not stand. Instead, I sat there on my stool, looking at them.

One by one, they circled in front of me, like some ritual. The Inspection of the Pigs by the Artist, I thought. I debated going to sleep where I sat or somehow, impossibly, hauling myself up the stairs and into my own bed. The pigs shuffled around each other, and admired my bright-inked creations on their backs. And I found myself dreaming. I dreamed that I sat there watching while Wilbur went to the door and nosed it open, the pigs slipping out into the yard and making their way to the house, where Wilbur repeated his performance and one by one they slipped inside the door.

And then I shook myself awake, and stumbled to my feet. The door was wide open and the pigs were gone, so I scrambled out to the yard to see it empty as well. Up on Jilly's balcony, movement caught my eye and the French doors shuddered open. A shadow lifted from the balcony, an impossible boxy shadow that floated across the sky, blocking out the clouds that outlined it in pearly tones.

As the moonlight struck it, I saw what it was. Jilly's brass bed, the frame supported on either side by three flying pigs. Their wings beat the air in tandem while she sat upright, her face moonlight bright with wonder as she gazed forward.

Did she notice me, did she wave? I'm not sure, because clouds obscured the view as she rose higher and higher into the sky. I'd like to think she didn't – that she knew Mrs. H. and I would take care of each other, and that she didn't need to look back. I like to think that every inch of her attention was focused on the journey, on that marvelous moment when we both learned that pigs could fly.

CHAPTER 10
BEGINNING

What it is

A beginning is a lovely place to start a story, even if you don't have the faintest clue what will happen in the end. In many ways, it's like working with a scene, so much of that earlier section will apply, but a beginning also sets up much of what will take place in the story, both at the level of the action and at the level of the meta-narrative and how the story is told.

What it provides

A story beginning gives you three of the key factors for a story: character, conflict, and setting. It probably also tells you something about tone, style, and genre. A beginning is the place where you convince the reader to give themselves over to you, to trust you to buckle them into the funhouse ride you've created and to know you won't let them go off the rails.

Considerations

Is this actually the beginning?

What does it predict about the ending?

Is it in the point of view that tells the story the most effectively?

What mood does it set? How can you make it more so?

One of the things that's sometimes useful is to think in terms of what works and how to make it more so. My favorite comparison is Spinal Tap's turning the knobs to 11. Find what is working in the story and turn those knobs to 11.

Pitfalls

It's an incomplete beginning and does not in fact give you character, conflict, and setting, but (hopefully) one or two of them.

It's familiar. Story beginnings create expectations for a reader and your task is to surprise them while not jarring them by breaking narrative conventions.

Sometimes you may, when starting with a beginning, impose an unnecessary frame story around the narrative. Why does this happen? I don't know but I've seen it happen multiple times. A frame story must play into the story it frames in such a way that by the time we reach the end of the internal story, we either have had our understanding of the frame change or we are about to witness a moment of revelation that causes such a change in understanding.

Next steps

Write the ending that the beginning predicts. Once you have that, you can begin constructing the intermediary scenes. Or, if you are uncomfortable writing out of consecutive order, write the next scene, then the next, etcetera, until you come to the ending.

Do try turning the knob to 11. What about the beginning appealed to you? If you were reading a story that started this way, what would you want it to deliver? What's nifty about it?

Exercises

1. Go through your beginning to determine how well you're setting up the world. Make a list of a) the sensory details, b) physical objects referenced, 3) places where spatial relationships are established, and 4) active verbs. If this is quickly done because you have left stuff out, you may want to rectify the situation. OA: Do this for 2-3 professional stories and compare with the list for yours.
2. Go through your beginning to determine how well you're setting up the character(s). Make a list of a) moments where we are connected to the character's internal thoughts, 2) description that reveals something about a character, c) dialogue that reveals something about a character, d) moments that communicate what a character wants. As with the previous exercise, if this is quickly done because you have left stuff out, you may want to fix that. OA: Do this for 2-3 professional stories and compare with the list for yours.
3. Go through your beginning to see what sort of conflict you're setting up. What are the problems or stresses that are implicit in the scene? What does each character want that they don't have, and how are they being kept from achieving it? OA: Make sure that each and every character has a want and conflict that is shown somewhere in the course of the beginning.

Case study: (The Dead Girl's Wedding March)

"The Dead Girl's Wedding March", which originally appeared in *Fantasy Magazine*, began by sitting down and writing once upon a time, and from there the beginning that quickly emerged: a rat proposing to a zombie girl. After that I had to figure out some questions: why does he want her, how did he find her, and why doesn't she want him? This story was my first sale to Fantasy Magazine, and Jeff VanderMeer approached me about collaborating on "The Surgeon's Tale" after reading it, so it's always been a particularly meaningful story, but it's also the first time I consciously set a story in the world of Tabat, which had previously only been a game world.

The Dead Girl's Wedding March

Once upon a time a dead girl lived with the other zombies in the caverns below the port of Tabat, in the city beneath that seaside town, the city that has no name. Thousands of years ago, the Wizard Sulooman plunged the city, buildings and all, into the depths of the earth, and removed its name, over some slight that no one but his ghost remembers. There life continues.

Some dead folk surrender to slumber, feeling that there is no point pretending an agenda for each day. A few, though, pace out their days in the way they once paced out their lives.

The only actual living things in the City of the Dead are the sleek, silver-furred rats that slip through its streets like reversed shadows. On a day there like any other day, a rat addressed the dead girl.

Her name was Zuleika, and she was dark-haired, dark-eyed, and smelled only faintly of the grave, because every evening she bathed in the river that flowed silently beneath her window.

"Marry me," the rat said. It stood upright on its back legs, its tail curled neatly around its feet.

She was pretending to eat breakfast. A pot steamed on the table. She poured herself a deliberate cup of chocolate before speaking.

"Why should I marry you?"

The rat eyed her. "To be sure," it admitted. "There's more in it for me than for you. Having a bride of your stature would increase mine, so to speak." It chuckled, smoothing its whiskers with a paw.

"I fear I must decline," she said.

Leaving the rat to console itself with muffins, she went into the parlor where her father sat reading the same paper he read every morning, its pages black rectangles.

"I have had a marriage proposal," she told him.

He folded his paper and set it down, frowning. "From whom?"

"A rat, just now. At breakfast."

"What does he expect? A dowry of cheese?"

She remembered not liking her father very much when she was alive.

"I told him no," she said.

He reached for his paper again. "Of course you did. You've never been in love and never will be. There is no change in this city. Indeed, it would be the destruction of us all. Shut the door when you go out."

***

She went shopping, carrying a basket woven from the white reeds that line the river's banks.

Passing through a clutter of stalls, she fingered fabrics lying in drifts: sleepy soft velvet, watery charmeuse, suedes as tender as a mouse's ear. All in shades of black and gray, whites lying among them like discarded moonlight.

The rat sat on the table's edge.

"I can provide well for you," it said. "Fish guts from the docks of Tabat and spoiled meat from its alleyways. I would bring you the orchard's gleanings: squishy apricot and rotted peaches, apples brown as bone and flat as the withered breasts of a crone. I would bring you bits of ripe leather from the tannery, soaked in a soup of pigeon shit and water until it is soft as flesh."

"Why me?" she asked. "Have I given you reason to suspect I would accept your advances?"

It stroked its whiskers in embarrassment. "No," it admitted. "I witnessed you bathing in the river, and saw the touch of iridescence that gilds your limbs, like plump white cheeses floating in the water. I felt desire so strong that I pissed myself, as though my bones had turned to liquid and were flowing out of me. I must have you for my wife."

She looked around at the market she had visited each third day for as long as she had been dead. At the tables of wares that never changed but only endlessly rearranged their elements. Then back at the rat.

"You may walk with me," she said.

The rat hopped into the basket and they strolled along in silence. At length, he began to speak.

He told her of the rats of the city without a name, who have lived so long so close to magic that it has seeped into their skin, their eyes, and down into their very guts. How they have seen their civilizations rise and fall over the centuries, and their sorcerers and magicians have learned cunning magics, only to see them torn away each time they re-descended into savagery. How the white-furred rat matrons ruled their current society, sending their swains out to gather them food, eating more and more, in order to gain greater and greater social weight.

"That is what first drew me to this idea," he said. "A human bride would have more weight than any of them. But then when I saw you, it seemed a meaningless and stale calculation."

She felt a thrill of warmth somewhere in her chest. Upon reflection she realized that it was an emotion that she had not felt before she died. It was part interest, and part intrigue, and part vanity, and part something else: a twinge of affection for this rat that promised to make her his world.

***

"There is no question," her father said. "This would bring change to the City."

"And?"

"And! Do you wish to destroy this place? We are held by the Wizard's spell – fixed in a moment when, dying because we cannot change, we do not die because we cannot change."

Zuleika frowned. "That makes no sense."

"That's because you're young."

"You have only forty years more than my own five thousand, three hundred and twelve. Surely when one considers the years I have lived, I can be reckoned an adult."

"You would think so, if you overlooked the fact that you will always be fifteen."

She stamped her foot and pouted, but centuries can jade even the most indulgent father. He sent for a Physician.

The Physician came with eager steps, for new cases were few and far between. He insisted on examining Zuleika from head to toe, and would have had her disrobe, save for her father's protest.

"She seems well enough to me," the Physician said in a disappointed tone.

"She believes she wishes to marry."

"Tut, tut," the Physician said in astonishment. "Well now. Love. And you wish this cured?"

"Before the contagion spreads any further or drives her to actions imperiling us all."

Zuleika said nothing. She was well aware she was not in love with the rat. But the idea of change had seized her like a fever.

The Physician overlaid her scalp with a netting of silver wire. Magnets hung like awkward beads amid crystals of midnight onyx and grey feldspar.

"It is a subtle stimulation," he murmured. "And certainly Love is not a subtle energy. But given sufficient time, it will work."

He directed that Zuleika sit in a chair in the parlor without disturbing the netting for three days.

The days passed slowly. Zuleika kept her eyes fixed on the window, which framed a cloudless, sunless, skyless world. She could feel the magnetic energies pulling her thoughts this way and that, but it seemed to her things remained much the same overall.

On the third day, the rat appeared.

"My beautiful fiancée," it said, gazing at where she sat. "What is that thing you wear?"

"It is a mechanism to remove Love," she said.

Its whiskers perked forward, and it looked pleased. "So you are in love?"

"No," she said. "But my father believes that I am."

"Hmmph," said the rat. "Tell me, what is the effect of such a mechanism if you are not in love?"

"I don't know."

It considered, absently flicking its tail.

"Perhaps it will have the opposite effect," it said.

"I have been thinking about that myself," she said. "Indeed, I feel fonder towards you with every passing moment."

"How much longer must you wear it?"

Her eyes sought the clock. "Another hour," she said.

"Then we must wait and see." The rat sniffed the air. "Did your family have muffins again this morning?" "I've been sitting here for three days; I didn't have breakfast."

"Then I shall be back within a half hour or so," it said and withdrew.

At the hour, the door opened, and her father and the Physician entered. The rat, licking its chops, discreetly moved beneath her chair where, hidden by her skirts, it could not be seen.

"Well, my daughter," her father said, patting her on the back as the Physician removed the apparatus. "Do you feel restored?"

"Indeed I do," she said.

"Good, good!" He clapped the Physician's shoulder, looking pleased. "Good work, man. Shall we retire to discuss your fee?"

The Physician looked at Zuleika. "Perhaps another examination..." he ventured.

"No need," her father said briskly. "Love removed, everything's fixed. Our city can continue on as it has for the past millennium."

***

When they had gone, the rat crept out from beneath her chair, regarding her. "Well?" it said.

"I do not wish to be married down here."

"We can make our way to the surface and say our vows in Tabat," the rat said. "I know all the tunnels, and where they wind to."

And so she took a lantern from where it hung in the garden, shedding its dim light over the pale vegetation nourished there by sorcery rather than sunlight. They made their way to the first tunnel entrance, the rat riding on her shoulder, and started towards the surface. Behind them, there came a massive crash and crack.

“What was that?” the rat said.

“Nothing,” Zuleika said. “Nothing at all, anymore.”

She marched on and behind her, the City with No Name continued to fall.

CHAPTER 11
ENDING

What it is

An ending tells you one of the most important things you can know about a story: what happens. What's a little more elusive in such cases is how you got there. But all in all, an ending can be more informative than a beginning, since it usually ties up all loose ends in the story, including those introduced at the beginning as well as those which occur over the course of the story.

One way that you might think of it is an old fashioned scale, the kind that weighs one object against another. Your ending is on one side of the scale. What do you need to include on the other side in your beginning in order to make the two sides balance? If there is high emotional impact in the end, then the beginning needs to make it clear that such an impact is within the realm of the story's possibility. Similarly, a comic ending needs to have a beginning that signals that possibility—usually by being comic itself.

What it provides

An ending tells you what has changed, which may or may not be helpful in determining how it was that it changed. It gives you the final moment of the story where the pay-off is delivered. While it does not tell you exactly how tension has been created in the story, it gives you significant clues to their creation and narrows down many of the possibilities.

Considerations

Is this really the ending or some other moment? Endings have a special resonance that signals to the reader that this is the end. A good ending lets the reader hear the "click" of the door to the story closing so they can find themself standing outside it, still thinking about the story's last moments.

Does it have the impact that a story needs in an ending? The ending is usually the payout for all the work you've done constructing the story. It must feel meaningful, as though its circumstances have grown out of the actions and choices that have occurred over the story's course, rather than a random happening.

What are you delivering on? Endings satisfy us on one level because they are the answer to the question posed to us at a story's beginning: given this set of factors, how will the author get us to the ending we expect? That's one reason deus ex machina endings are unsatisfying; they require little effort on a writer's part.

Pitfalls

Too much is going on. Everything but the kitchen sink appears in the story and you're not sure what to do with any of it. In this case, start trying to locate the main character and main source of conflict, and see if there are pieces that might get set aside for other stories. In extreme cases, you may be dealing with a book instead of a short story, in which case you're going to want to apply a process suited to developing novels, i.e. creating an outline.

Not enough is going on. There your characters are on a beach, sipping margaritas, and saying, "Well, now that's all over." In this case you're going to have to think about your penultimate scene (the one before the final one) and treat that as your climactic ending. What needs to have happened during the story for the protagonist to deserve the margarita?

Next steps

Make a list of what is established in the ending and figure out the questions that each thing is answering.

Think of unexpected ways to arrive at the events of the ending. If the house is in ashes, what are interesting circumstances under which the fire could have started?

Think about what is delivered to the main character and how it represents or answers their wants and needs. Is there any way in which characters have been thwarted?

Exercises

1. Write 250-500 words of your main character reflecting about the events of the story, and their personal significance. How do they interpret the events and just as importantly, how do they feel about them? OA: Do this for all the characters.
2. Is there a central image to the ending, something that is referenced throughout? Write out a way you could use it elsewhere in the work. OA version: Figure out three ways to do so. You do not need to actually include them in the finished work if it starts feeling like overkill, but do figure out a way they could have been included.
3. Set up an echo. Where can you begin your story in such a way that it foreshadows this ending? Perhaps it takes place in the same location, or at the same time of day or year. OA: Have multiple echoes throughout the story.

Case study: (The Subtler Art)

I wrote "The Subtler Art" for an anthology called *Blackguards* and started with the ending: the final moments of a bet, lost by both participants, and what the Dark says in conclusion. That gave me the two main characters and something of their personalities; it made sense for them to be arguing over which of them practiced the most subtle art. It also gave me the setting, and the main thing that I had to figure out was how the bet arose in the first place. This gave me the character of Cathay, and once I had them, the rest of the pieces fell into place.

This is the second story I wrote in the setting of the city of Serendib, and I will say that putting multiple stories in a particular setting is, in my opinion, a useful habit. Stories often tend to spark other stories, and if you're at a loss for ideas, going back to a world that you've enjoyed writing in before will often give you a starting point for something else in that setting.

The Subtler Art

Anything can happen in Serendib, the city built of dimensions intersecting, and this is what happened there once.

The noodle shop that lies on the border between the neighborhood of Yddle, which is really a forest, houses strapped to the wide trunks, and Eclect, an industrial quarter, is claimed by both, with equally little reason.

The shop was its own Territory, with laws differing from either area, but the same can be said of many eating establishments in the City of a Thousand Parts. But the noodles were hand shaved, and the sauce was made of minced ginger and chopped green onions with a little soy sauce and a dash of enlightenment, and they were unequaled in Serendib.

It was the Dark's favorite place to eat, and since she and Tericatus were haphazard cooks at best and capable of (usually accidentally) killing someone at worst, they often ate their meals out. And because the city is so full of notorious people, very few noted that the woman once known as the best assassin on five continents on a world that only held four and her lover, a wizard who'd in his time achieved wonders and miracles and once even a rebirthed God, were slurping noodles only an elbow length's away at the same chipped beige stone counter.

Though indifferent cooks, both were fond enough of food to argue its nuances in detail, and this day they were arguing over the use of white pepper or golden when eating the silvery little fish that swarm every seventh Spring in Serendib.

"Yellow pepper has a flatness to it," Dark argued. Since retirement, she had let herself accumulate a little extra fat over her wiry muscles, and a few white strands traced themselves through her midnight hair, but she remained the one of the pair who drew most eyes. Her lover was a lean man, sparse in flesh and hair, gangly, with long capable hands spotted with unnatural colors and burns from alchemical experiments.

"Cooking," said the person on the other side of her, "is an exceedingly subtle art."

"Cathay," the Dark said, recognizing the stranger. Her tone was cool. The newcomer was both acquaintance and former lover for both of them, but more than that, Cathay was a Trickster mage, and you never knew what she might be getting into.

Tericatus grunted his own acknowledgment and greeting, rolling an eye sideways at the Dark in warning. He knew she was prone to impatience and while Tricksters can play with many things, impatience is a favorite point to press on.

But the conversation that the Trickster made was slight, as though Cathay's mind were elsewhere, and by the time the other had tapped coin to counter in order to pay, most of what she'd said had vanished, except for those few words.

"A subtle art," the Dark repeated to Tericatus, letting the words linger like pepper on her tongue. "It describes what I do as well. The most subtle art of all, assassination."

Tericatus slouched back in his chair with a smile on his lips and a challenging quirk to his eyebrow. "A subtle art, but surely not the most subtle. That would be magery, which is subtlety embodied."

The Dark looked hard at her mate. While she loved him above almost all things, she had been – and remained – very proud of her skill at her profession.

The argument hung in the air between them. They both considered it. So many words could go in defense of either side. But actions speak stronger than words. And so they both stood and slid a token beneath their empty bowls and nodded at each other in total agreement.

"Who first?" the Dark asked.

"I have one in mind already, if you don't care," Tericatus murmured.

"Very well."

***

Serendib has no center – or at least the legend goes that if anyone ever finds it, the city will fall – but surely wherever its heart is, it must lie close to the gardens of Caran Sul.

Their gates are built of white moon-metal, which grows darker whenever the moon is shadowed, and their grounds are overgrown with shanks of dry green leaves and withered purple blossoms that smell sweet and salty, like the very edges of the sea.

In the center five towers start to reach to the sky, only to tangle into the form of Castle Knot, where the Angry Daughters, descended from the prophet who once lived there, swarm, and occasionally pull passersby into their skyborne nests, never to be seen again.

Tericatus and the Dark paid their admittance coin to the sleepy attendant at the entrance stile outside the gate and entered through the pathway hacked into the vegetation. Tericatus paused halfway down the tunnel to lean down and pick up a caterpillar from the dusty path, transferring it to the dry leaves on the opposite side.

The Dark kept a wary eye on the sky as they emerged into sunlight. While she did not fear an encounter with a few of the Daughters, a crowd of them would be an entirely different thing. But nothing stirred in the stony coils and twists so far above.

"This reminds me," she ventured, "of the time we infiltrated the demon city of S'keral pretending to be visiting scholars and wrestled that purple stone free from that idol."

"Indeed," Tericatus said, "this is nothing like that."

"Ah. Perhaps it is more like the time we entered the village of shapeshifters and killed their leaders before anyone had time enough to react."

"It is not like that either," Tericatus said, a little irritably.

"Remind me," she said, "exactly what we are doing here."

Tericatus stopped and crossed his arms. "I'm demonstrating the subtlety with which magic can work."

"And how exactly will it work? she inquired.

He unfolded an arm and pointed upward towards the dark shapes flapping their way down from the heights, clacking the brazen, razor-sharp bills on the masks they wore.

"I presume you don't need me to do anything."

Tericatus did not deign to answer.

The shapes continued to descend. The Dark could see the brass claws tipping their gloves, each stained with ominous rust.

"You're quite sure you don't need me?"

A butterfly fluttered across the sky from behind them. Dodging to catch it in her talons, one Daughter collided with another, and the pair tumbled into the path of a third, then a fourth...

The Dark blinked as the long grass around them filled with fallen bodies.

"Very nice," she said with genuine appreciation. "And the tipping point?"

Tericatus smirked slightly. "The caterpillar. You may have noticed that I moved it from one kind of plant to another -"

"Of course."

"And when it eats jilla leaves, its scent changes, attracting adults of its species to come lay more eggs there."

"Well done," she said. "A valiant try indeed."

***

The Home for Dictators is, despite its name, a retirement home, though it is true that it holds plenty of past leaders of all sorts of stripes, and many of them are not particularly benign.

"Why here?" Tericatus said as they came up Fume and Spray and Rant Street, changing elevations as they went till the air grew chill and dry.

"It grates on me to perform a hit without getting paid for it," the Dark said, a little apologetically. "It feels unprofessional."

"You're retired. Why should you worry about feeling unprofessional?"

"You're retired too. Why should you worry about who's more subtle?"

"Technically, wizards never retire."

"Assassins do," the Dark said. "It's just that we don't usually get the chance."

"Get the chance or lose the itch?"

She shrugged. "A little of both?"

Tericatus expected the Dark to go in through the back in the way she'd been famous for: unseen, unannounced. Or failing that, to disguise herself in one of her many cunning alterations: an elderly inmate to be admitted, a child come to visit a grandparent, a dignitary there to honor some old politician. But instead she marched up the steps and signed her name in bold letters on the guestbook. "The Dark."

The receptionist/nurse, a young newtling with damp, pallid skin and limpid eyes, spun it around to read the name, which clearly meant little to him. "And you've come to see..." he said, letting the sentence trail upward in question as his head tilted.

The Dark eyed him. It was a look Tericatus knew well, a look that started mild and reasonable but which, as time progressed, would swell into menace, darken like clouds gathering on the edge of the horizon. The newt paled, cheeks twitching convulsively as it swallowed.

"Simply announce me to the populace at large," the Dark said.

Without taking his eyes from her, the newt fumbled for the intercom, a device clearly borrowed from some slightly more but not too advanced dimension, laden with black-iron cogs and the faint green glow of phlogiston. He said hesitantly into the bell-like speaking cup, "The, uh, Dark is here to see, uh, someone."

The Dark smiled faintly and turned back to the waiting room.

After a few moments, Tericatus said, "Are we expecting someone?"

"Not really," the Dark replied.

"Some thing?"

"Closer, but not quite," she said.

They glanced around as a bustle of doctors went through a doorway.

"There we go," the Dark said. She tugged her lover in their wake.

Up a set of stairs and then they saw the doctors gathered in a room at the head where an elderly woman lay motionless in her bed.

"The Witch of the Southeast," Dark murmured. "She's always feared me, and her heart was frail as tissue paper. Come on."

They drifted further along the corridor. Dark paused in a doorway. The man in the wheelchair wore an admiral's uniform, but his eyes were unseeing, his lips drawn up in a rictus that exposed purple gums.

"Diploberry," Dark said. "It keeps well, and just a little has the effect one wants. It is a relatively painless means of suicide."

Teracitus looked at the admiral. "Because he heard you were coming."

The Dark spread her hands in a helpless shrug, her grin fox sly.

"And you're getting paid for all of them? How long ago did you plant some of the seeds you've harvested here?"

"The longest would be a decade and a half," she mused.

"How many others have died?"

"Three. All dictators whose former victims were more than willing to see their old oppressors gone."

Tericatus protested, "You can't predict that with such finesse."

"Can I not?" she asked, and pointed at the door where three stretchers were exiting, carried by orderlies in the costume of the place, gold braids and silver sharkskin suits.

She smiled smugly. "Subtle, no?"

Tericatus nodded, frowning.

"Come now," she said. "Is it that hard to admit defeat?"

"Not so hard, my love," he said. "But isn't that Cathay?"

Dark felt another touch of unease. You never know what a Trickster Mage is getting you into. And there indeed stood Cathay at the front desk, speaking sweetly to someone, a bouquet of withered purple blossom in her hand, more of it in her hair, a smell like longing and regret and the endless sea.

Dark murmured, "She always loved those flowers and yet did not like contending with the Daughters."

Tericatus said, "She had lovers here, I know that. No doubt she has five inheritances coming."

Cathay turned and smiled at them. The Dark bowed slightly, and Tericatus inclined his head.

***

"But," the Dark finally said into the silence as they walked away, headed by mutual accord to the bar closest to the noodle shop, "we can still argue over which of us exercises the second most subtle art."

CHAPTER 12
TITLES

What it is

Starting a story with a title is as close to starting with a blank page as you can get. You've picked the color and consistency of the paper, but what emerges next is anyone's guess.

Karen Joy Fowler says that a good title is one where your understanding of it has entirely changed by the time you have finished the story. So—what's the first way that leaps to mind to read your title, and what other ways are possible? (Case in point, Fowler's wonderful novel *We Are All Completely Beside Ourselves*, which I highly recommend.)

Can you have a good story without a good title? Sure, but why hamper it in that way? Sometimes a title is the very last thing that I think of. If I come up with a great one, then I try to write a story that will live up to it.

What it provides

Very little.

Considerations

What does the title promise in terms of style? Does it fall in a particular camp of writing? Does it promise a simple or a complex story?

What does the title promise the reader in terms of emotional tone? Will it be sad, funny, bittersweet...what? Can you read it with two different tones and manage to combine them in the piece?

How does the title relate to the overall point of the story? How can you sneak it in if you need to?

What are the connotations of the word or phrase? Connotations are additional ideas or feelings evoked by the word(s) in addition to the primary meaning.

Does it contain any interesting metaphors that you can exploit?

Pitfalls

Is the title too abstract or basic? Does it give you nothing to hang a story on? In that case try to find associations with other words or perhaps introduce a random element that complicates the title in some way.

Is the title too coyly meta, something like "The Author Doesn't Want to Tell You This" or "My Parents Went to Mars And All I Got Was this Lousy T-shirt Slogan"? Save it for a blog post perhaps.

Is the title one word? That may make it hard to find something, or it may yield way too many possibilities, in which case you'll probably want to narrow it down substantially?=.

Is the title "The Something"? The blandness of that structure when "something" isn't a truly interesting word, makes that difficult to pull off.

Flailing. There's too many ways to read the title and you can't seem to pick one. Apologies but you must. You can always (try to) add some of the other stuff into the more fleshed out draft, but for now, select your antelope from the herd and pursue it wholeheartedly before you begin eying any others.

Being overly constricted. The title is so specific and weird that you cannot think of anything that actually fits.

With any title that's not yielding a story easily, remember that putting it in a file for later is a valid move. You haven't invested much time in it so far. This actually is a good exercise for generating something that may help you prime the pump next time your internal word well is running a little dry: either write down 30 titles, pulling them out of your head, or else use some random method to generate 30. If none of them create any ideas in your head, put them in your folder for unfinished stuff and try doing it again a few more times.

Next steps

Take the title and jot down a list of 5-10 ways in which it might be interpreted. Is there a natural progression between two of those understandings, i.e. the story might seem at first to be about love, but by the end is about death?

You need to figure out what the story is - the characters, the plot, and the setting. Work towards doing that in two or three sentences, then expand outward, turning those words into a 250-500 word synopsis. Take the synopsis and split it up into scenes.

Exercises

1. On the Nebula Award website (nebulas.sfwa.org), find the list of past titles for the Nebula Award winning short story. Go and read two or three of them. What does the title do to create expectations for the story? How does your understanding of the title change from the time before you have read the story and afterward? OA: repeat multiple times.)
2. Write out the titles of all of your finished stories on a single page. What patterns do you notice? OA: include your unfinished ones as well.
3. Investigate the history of your words by looking them up in a good dictionary. Think about morphology, the study of how

words are put together and how they relate to other words in the same language. Are there related words in the same language or words that share the same root in some way? OA: Learn more about morphology.

Case study: (I'll Gnaw Your Bones, the Manticore Said)

"I'll Gnaw Your Bones, the Manticore Said" was a phrase that came to me one day and seemed like an intriguing title. The strategy I took was a fairly straightforward one: I had a manticore saying the words of the title, but subverted it at the same time so reader expectations were thwarted, while added them an even more interesting manticore than any they might have pre-constructed: simple-minded, farting, loyal Bupus, one of the few actual allies the narrator has.

I'll Gnaw Your Bones, the Manticore Said

Even Duga the Prestidigitator, who never pays much attention to anything outside his own hands, raised an eyebrow when I announced I'd be hooking the manticore up to my wagon.

"Isn't that dangerous?" my husband Rik said. He steepled his fingers, regarding me.

"The more we have pulling, the faster we get there," I pointed out. "And Bupus has been getting fat and lazy as a tabby cat. No one pays to see a fat manticore."

"More dangerous than any tabby cat," Rik said.

I knew what he meant, but I kept a lightning rod at hand in the wagon seat in case of trouble. Bupus knew I'd scorch his greasy whiskers if he crossed me.

There is a tacit understanding between a beast trainer and her charges, whether it be great cats, cunning dragons, or apes and other man-like creatures. They know, and the trainer knows, that as long as certain lines aren't crossed, that if expectations are met, everything will be fine and no one will get hurt.

That's not to say I didn't keep an eye on Bupus, watching for a certain twitch to his tail, the way one bulbous eye would go askew when anger was brewing. A beast's a beast, after all, and not responsible for what they do when circumstances push them too far. Beasts still, no matter how they speak or smile or woo.

At any rate, Bupus felt obliged to maintain his reputation whenever another wagon or traveler was in earshot.

"Gnaw your bones," he rumbled, rolling a vast oversized eyeball back at me. The woman he was trying to impress shrieked and dropped her chickens, which vanished in a white flutter among the blackberry vines and ferns that began where the road's ground stone gave way to forest. A blue-headed jay screamed in alarm from a pine.

"Behave yourself," I said.

He rumbled again, but nothing coherent, just a low, animal sound.

We were coming up on Piperville, which sits on a trade hub. Steel figured we'd pitch there for a week, get a little silver sparkling in our coffers, eat well a few nights.

It had been a lean winter and times were hard all over – traveling up from Ponce's Spring, we'd found slim pickings and indifferent audiences too worried about the dust storms to pay any attention to even our best: Laxmi the elephant dancing in pink spangles to "Waltzing Genevieve", the pyramid of crocodiles that we froze and unfroze each performance via a lens-and-clockwork basilisk, the Unicorn Maiden, and of course, my manticore.

Rik was driving a wagon full of machinery, packed and protected from the dust with layers of waxed canvas. He pulled up near me, so we were riding in tandem for a bit. No one was coming the opposite way for now. We'd hit some road traffic coming out of Ponce's, but now it was only occasional, a twice an hour thing at most.

"You know what I'm looking forward to?" I called over to him.

He considered. I watched him thinking in the sunlight, my broad-shouldered and beautiful husband and just the look of him, his long scholar's nose and silky beard, made me smile.

"Beer," he said finally. "And clean sheets. Cleeaaaan sheets." He drawled out the last words, smiling over at me.

"A bath," I said.

A heartfelt groan so deep it might have come from the bottom of his soul came from him. "Oh, a bath. With towels. Thick towels."

I was equally enraptured by the thought, so much so that I didn't notice the wheel working loose. And Bupus, concerned with looking for people to impress, didn't warn me. With a sideways lurch, the wagon tilted, and the wheel kept going, rolling down the roadway, neat as you please, until it passed Laxmi and she put out her trunk and snagged it.

I put on my shoes and hopped down to examine the damage. Steel heard the commotion and came back from the front of the train. He rode Beulah, the big white horse that accompanies him in the ring each time. Sometimes we laugh about how attached he is to that horse, but never where he can hear us.

The carts and caravans kept passing us. A few waved and Rik waved back. The august clowns were practicing their routine, somersaulting into the dust behind their wagon, then running to catch up with it again. Duga was practicing card tricks while his assistant drove, dividing her attention between the reins and watching him. Duga was notoriously close-mouthed about his methods; I suspected watching might be her only way to learn.

"Whaddya need?" Steel growled as he reached me.

"Looks like a linch pin fell out. Could have been a while back. Sparky'll have a new one, I'm sure."

His blue gaze slid skyward, sideways, anywhere to avoid meeting my eyes. "Sparky's gone."

It is an unfortunate fact that circuses are usually made of Family and outsiders – jossers, they call us. Steel treated Family well but was unwilling to extend that courtesy outside the circle. I'd married in, and he was forced to acknowledge me, but Sparky had been a full outsider, and Steel had made his life a misery, maintaining our cranky and antiquidated machines: the fortune teller, the tent-lifter, and Steel's pride and joy, the spinning cups, packed now on the largest wagon and pulled by Laxmi and three oxen.

The position of circus smith had been vacant of Family for a while now, ever since Big Joy fell in love with a fire-eater and left us for the Whistling Piskie – a small, one-ring outfit that worked the coast.

So we'd lost Sparky because Steel had scrimped and shorted his wages, not to mention refusing to pay prentice fees when he wanted to take one on. More importantly, we'd lost his little traveling cart, full of tools and scrap and spare linchpins.

"So what am I going to do?" I snapped. Bupus had sat down on the road and was eying the passing caravans, more out of curiosity than hunger or desire to menace. "I'll gnaw your bones," he said almost conversationally, but it frightened no one in earshot. He sighed and settled his head between his paws, a green snot dribble bubbling from one kitten-sized nostril.

The Unicorn Girl pulled up her caravan. She'd been trying to repaint it the night before and there were bleary splotches of green and lavender paint splotching its sides.

"What's going on?' she said loudly. "Driving badly again, Tara?"

The Unicorn Girl was one of those souls with no volume control. Sitting next to her in tavern or while driving was painful. She'd bray the same stories over and over again, and was tactless and unkind. I tried to avoid her when I could.

But, oh, she pulled them in. That long, narrow, angelic face, the pearly horn emerging from her forehead, and two lush lips, peach-ripe, set like emerging sins beneath the springs of her innocent doe-like eyes.

Even now, she looked like an angel, but I knew she was just looking for gossip, something she might be able to use to buy favor or twist like a knife when necessary.

Steel looked back and forth. "Broken wagon, Lily," he said. "You can move along."

She dimpled, pursing her lips at him but took up her reins. The two white mares pulling her wagon were daughters of the one he rode, twins with a bad case of the wobbles but which should be good for years more, if you ignored the faint, constant trembling of their front legs. Most people didn't notice it.

"She needs to learn to mind her tongue," I said.

"Rik needs to come in with us," Steel said, ignoring my comment. "He's the smartest, he knows how to bargain. These little towns have their own customs and laws and it's too easy to set a foot awry and land ourselves in trouble."

Much as I hated to admit, Steel was right. Rik is the smartest of the lot, and he knows trade law like the back of his hand.

"I'll find someone to leave with you, and Rik will ride back with the pin, soon as he can," Steel said.

"All right," I said. Then, as he started to wheel Beulah around. "Someone I won't mind, Steel. Got me?"

"Got it," he said, and rode away.

"I don't like leaving you," Rik said guiltily. It was a year old story, and its once upon a time had begun on our honeymoon night, with him riding out to help with the funeral of his grandfather, who had been driven into a fatal apoplectic fit by news of his marriage to someone who'd never known circus life.

"Can't be helped," I said crisply. He sighed.

"Tara..."

"Can't be helped." I flapped an arm at him, go on, get along, faster you are to town, faster you're back to me."

He got out of his wagon long enough to kiss me and ruffle my hair. "Not long," he said. "I won't be long."

***

"We'll leave Preddi with you," Steel said, a quarter hour after I'd watched Rik's caravan recede into the distance. It had taken a while for the rest of the circus to pass me, wagon after wagon. Even for such a small outfit, we had a lot of wagons.

Preddi was Rik's father, a small, stooped man given to carelessness with his dress. He was a kindly man, I think, but difficult to get to know because his deafness distanced him.

We pulled the wagon over to the side of the road, in a margined sward thick with yellow loosestrife and dandelions. A narrow deer path led through blackberry tangles and further into the pines, a stream coming through the thick pine needles and chuckling along the rocks. I tied Bupus to the wagon, and brought out a sack of hams and loaves of bread before making several trips in to bring him buckets of water.

Preddi settled himself on the grass and extracted a deck of greasy cards from the front pocket of his flannel shirt. While I worked, he laid out hand after hand, playing poker with himself, studying it.

The day wore on.

And on. I cleaned the wagon tack, and repacked the bundles in it, mainly my training gear. Someone else would be tending my cage of beasts when they pitched camp, and truth be told, anyone could, but I still preferred to be the one who feed the crocodiles, for example, and watched for mouth rot or the white lesions that signal pox virus and clean their cage thoroughly enough to make sure no infection could creep in under their scales or into the tender areas around their vents.

Bupus gorged himself and then slept, but roused enough to want to play. I threw the heavy leather ball and each time his tail whipped out with frightening speed and batted it aside. Fat and lazy, he may be, but Bupus has many years left in him. They go four or five decades, and I'd raised him from the shell ten years earlier, before I'd even bought the flimsy paper ticket that led me to meet Rik.

I hadn't known what I had at first. A sailor swapped me the egg in return for me covering his bar tab, and who knows who got the best of that bargain? I was a beast trainer for the Duke, and mainly I worked with little animals, trained squirrels and ferrets and marmosets. They juggled and danced, shot tiny plaster pistols, and engaged in duels as exquisite as any courtier's.

The egg was bigger than my doubled fists laid knuckle and palm to knuckle and palm. It was coarse to the touch, as though threads or hairy roots had been laid over the shell and grown into it, and it was a deep yellow, the same yellow that Bupus's eyes would open into, honey depths around clover-petaled pupils.

I kept it warm, near the hearth, but could not figure out what it might contain. Months later it hatched – lucky that I was there that day to feed the mewling, squawling hatchling chopped meat and warm milk. I wrapped the sting in padding and leather. Even then it struck out with surprising speed and strength. A manticore is a vulnerable creature, lacking human hands to defend the softness of its face, and the sting compensates for that vulnerability.

He talked a moon, perhaps a moon and a half later. I took him with me at first, when I was training the Duke's creatures, but a marmoset decided to investigate, and I learned then that a manticore's bite is a death grip, particularly with a marmoset's delicate bones between its teeth.

Some beast trainers dull their more intelligent beasts. It's an easy enough procedure, if you can drug or spell them unconscious. The knife is thin, more like a flattened awl than a blade, and you insert it at the corner of the eye, going behind the eyeball itself. Once you've pushed it in to the right depth, perforating the plate of the skull lying behind the eye, you swing back and forth holding it between thumb and forefinger, two cutting arcs. It bruises the eye, leaves it black and tender in the socket for days afterward, but it heals in time.

It doesn't kill their intelligence entirely, but they become simpler. More docile, easier to manage. They don't scheme or plot escape, and they're less likely to lash out. Done right, even a dragon can be made clement. And those beasts prone to over-talkativeness—dryads and mermaids, for the most part – can be rendered speechless or close to it.

I've never done that, though my father taught me the technique. I like my talking beasts, most of the time, and on occasion, I've had conversation with sphinx or lamia that were as close to talking with a person as could be.

After the marmoset incident, I left Bupus at home, the establishment the Duke allowed me, a fine place with stable and mews and even a heat-room, which the Ducal coal stores kept supplied all winter long and into the chilly Tabatian springs. I kept him in a stall that had been reinforced, and there were other animals to keep him company.

I'd gone to the circus to see their creatures. They had the crocodiles, which were nothing out of the ordinary, and the elephant, which was also unremarkable, since the Duchess kept two pygmy elephants in her menagerie. And an aging hippogriff, a splendid creature even though its primaries had gone gray with age long ago. I was surprised to his beak overgrown, as though no one had coped it in months.

"Look here," I said to the man standing to watch the cages and make sure no one poked a finger through and lost it. "Your hippogriff is badly tended. See how he rubs his beak along the ground, how he feaks? Your tender is careless, sir."

I was full of youth and indignation, but I softened when he perked up and said, "Can you tend them? We lost our fellow. How much would you charge?"

"No charge," I said. "If you let me look over the hippogriff as thoroughly as I'd like to. I haven't ever had the chance to get my hands on a live one."

"Can you come back later, when we close up?" He looked apologetic. He was a pretty man, and his uniform made him even prettier.

"I can." It'd mean a late night, but there was nothing going on that next morning – I could sleep in, and go to check the marmosets in the afternoon, or let the regular assistant do it, even, if I was feeling lazy.

So I came back late that night and pushed my way through the crowds eddying out, like a duck swimming against the current. He was waiting for me near the cages. I'd brought my bag of tools, and so we went from cage to cage.

He settled the hippogriff when it bated at the sight of me, flapping its wings and rearing upward. It was easily calmed, and he ran his fingers through the silky feathers around its eyes, rubbing softly over the scaly cere, until its eyes half-lidded and it chirped with pleasure, nuzzling its head along his side.

I trimmed its beak and claws and checked it over before moving on to the other animals. It took me three hours, and even so, much of that was simply telling Rik what would need to be done later on – to stop giving the crocodiles sardines, for example, before they got sick from the oiliness.

I refused pay, and he insisted that he should buy me a cup of wine, at least. How inevitable was it that I would take this beautiful man home with me?

In the morning, I showed my household to my lover. The dueling marmosets, the brace of piskies, the cockatrice kept by itself, lest it strike out in its bad temper. And Bupus, sprawled out across the courtyard. Rik was enchanted.

"A manticore!" he said. "I've never seen a tamed one. Or a wild one, for that matter. They come from the deserts in the land to the south, you know."

A year later, diffidently, while the caravan was spending a month in Tabat, he mentioned to me that the hippogriff had finally succumbed to old age and the caravan would like to buy Bupus.

I refused to sell, but when I married him, the manticore came with me.

When the sun touched down on the horizon and lingered there, like a marble being rolled back and forth beneath one's palm, we realized that there was some delay. If not tonight, though, they'd come tomorrow. Preddi and I discussed it all with shrugs and miming, agreeing to build a fire before the last of the sunlight vanished.

The woods that run beside the road there are dark and dangerous, which is why travelers stick to the road. As night had approached, there were no more passersby – everyone had found shelter where they could. Preddi and I would spread bedrolls beside the fire and keep watch in turns, but I wasn't worried much. The smell of a manticore keeps off most predators.

But as I picked through the limbs that lay like sutures across the ground's interwoven needles, a crackling through the dry leaves at the clearing's edge alerted me. Preddi was near the road, gathering more wood.

As I watched I saw stealthy movement. First one, then more, as though the shadows themselves were crawling towards me. As they emerged from the crevices beneath logs and the hollows of the trees, I saw a host of leprous, rotting rabbits, their fur blackened with drying blood, their eyes alight with foxfire. I did not know what malign force animated them, but it was clear it meant me no good.

Out of sight but not earshot, Bupus let out a simultaneous snore and long sonorous fart. Under other circumstances, it would have been funny, but now it only echoed flat and helpless as the rabbits, crouched as low to the ground as though they were snakes, writhed through the dry grasses towards me, their eyes gleaming with moon-touched luminescence.

The novelty of the sensation might have been what had me frozen. It was as though my belly were trying to crawl sideways, as though my bones had been stolen without my notice.

They were nearly to me, crawling in a sinuous motion, as though their flesh were liquid. Preddi wouldn't hear me shout. Neither would the snoring Bupus. I strained to scream nonetheless. It seemed unreasonable not to.

And then behind me there was a noise.

A woman was coming towards me along the deer path, dressed in the onion-skin colored gown of a Palmer, carrying an ancient throwlight. It was made of bronze, and aluminum capped one end, while the other bulged with a glass lens.

She thumbed its side and it shed its cold and mechanical light across the leprous rabbits, which recoiled as though a single mass. They smoldered under the unnatural light, withered away into ringlets of oily smoke.

"I saw your fire from the road," she said, letting the light play over the last of the rabbits. "This area is curse-ridden, and I thought you might not know to look out. Light kills them, though."

"Thank you," I said shakily. "Will you share our fire?"

"Yes," she said, as though expecting the invitation. She was a small woman with a head of short, crown-curled hair—slight but with enough weight to give her substance. No jewelry was evident, only the simplicity of her robe and the worn leather pack on her back, which she tucked her light back into.

"That's a useful thing," I said. "Where did you get it?"

"I found it," she said before changing the subject. "Are you unharmed? A bite from a curse creature can fester."

I shook my head. "They didn't get close enough," I said. "Good timing on your part."

Back at the fire, I tried to convey to Preddi that there was danger in the woods. I don't know if it got through or not. We built the fire up, and stacked the extra wood nearby, settling down to toast bread and cheese on sticks over the fire. Bupus whined for cheese, but it makes him ill, so I gave him chunks of almost-burned toasted bread instead. It's good for his digestion. He looked reproachful, but crunched them down.

The Palmer, whose name turned out to be Lupe, and I talked, Preddi's gaze moving between us as though he were listening, although when I tried to include him in the conversation, he gave me a blank look. I learned she was traveling from Port Wasp to Piperville, a Palmer, although she did not reveal the purpose of her pilgrimage. Well, that's a personal thing, and not one everyone shares, so I didn't push the question.

"You're a beast trainer," she said, eying me.

"I am – and my father before him, and his mother before him."

"A tradition in your family." Her eyes glittered in the firelight, malicious jet beads.

"Yes."

"Do you pass down lists of what are beasts and what are people?"

I sighed. One of those. "Look," I said. "We know which are beasts and which people. Beasts cannot overcome their natures and are not responsible for their actions. People can and are. There are four races of people: human, the Snake folk, the Dead beneath Tabat, and Angels, although no one has seen the last in centuries."

"But although beasts are helpless before their natures, should one kill a person, they are killed in turn."

"Of course," I said. "Any farmer knows that a dog that bites once will bite again. They cannot help it. People can learn, so they can be punished and learn from the experience."

She snorted and spat something fat and wet into the fire. "It's no use talking to you," she said. She turned to Preddi. "And what about you?" she said.

He looked at her blankly.

"He's a little deaf," I said.

"Ah." She leaned forward and shouted into his ear, putting a hand on his arm to steady herself.

He looked at her, surprised. Few of us talked to Preddi – too difficult to stand there loudly repeating a phrase until it penetrated the muffling of his hearing.

I stood up and went to see to Bupus.

He was lying on his back, sprawled out like a tomcat in hot weather. Spittle roped from his gaping mouth and his knobby, chitinous tail twitched in his sleep, its tip glistening with green ichor.

I checked him over for ticks, parasites, thorns and the like. He grumbled in his sleep, turning over when I thumped him, great flanks shivering as though bitten by invisible flies.

"Gnaw your bones," he muttered.

When I turned back to the fireside, I froze as deeply as I had with the rabbits. Off in the shadows beneath a sheltering pair of cedars, Preddi and the pilgrim woman were huddled together in his bedroll, moving in rhythm.

I was appalled on several levels. For one, you don't want to think about your husband's father like that. You know what I mean. Plus this woman didn't seem very pleasant. And this was awfully sudden, so I felt as though I should make sure she didn't chew off his face or turn out to be some sort of shifter. But above it all, I was irritated at their lack of manners. Was I supposed to act as though they weren't there on the other side of the fire? I could understand why they hadn't gone further, worried about the rabbits. But still. Still.

After they settled down, Preddi emerged and signaled he was ready to take his watch. He didn't look me in the face, nor was I sure what to say. I looked him over and if he'd been enchanted in some way, I couldn't tell, nor was I sure what the signs of such enchantment might be. So I tried to sleep, but mainly lay awake, wondering what Rik would say when he found out.

***

In the morning, Steel was there.

"Where's Rik?" I said, before any other business.

"There's been a little trouble," Steel said.

"What trouble?"

He flapped an irritated hand at me. "Get your manticore ready while I fix the axle." He gave Preddi and the pilgrim a glance.

"That's Lupe, a pilgrim," I said. "She saved my life last night."

He grunted and turned to the axle. I roused Bupus to get him into harness, grumbling under my breath.

Preddi and Lupe walked on one side of the wagon while Steel rode on the other. I drove. Lupe leaned on Preddi as they walked, and I noticed the slight hitch to her gait, as though one leg were shorter than the other.

"You can ride with me," I said, wondering if she'd be able to keep up otherwise. She shook her head, smiling at Preddi. It was a gesture that warmed me to her, despite my fears.

"What happened was this," Steel said. "Lily got two farmers all riled up and throwing insults at each other. They started swinging and then we got fined for disturbing the peace."

"Fined? How much?"

He winced.

"That much?" I said. "We don't have any cash to spare." Rik keeps the books for the circus, and I knew just how thin the financial razor's edge we danced on was.

"Yes," Steel said. "They let me out but kept the others in there. I'm supposed to raise the money. How, I don't know. Meanwhile, they're all sitting in jail eating their heads off and adding each day's room and board to the total."

"We have no extra money," I said.

"I know."

"I do," Lupe said from somewhere behind us. "I could help you."

We both turned to look at her, but Steel said the obvious thing first. "And what would you want in return?"

"A friend's wagon went into a gorge, two miles ahead. I need someone to go into it and bring out a box of tools that he needs. He'll come back later to retrieve the wagon itself, but he's gone ahead to Piperville. I stayed behind to see if I could get help in getting the wagon out, but had no luck. Now I just want to bring him his tools, but I am forbidden to go within walls during my journey."

It was flimsy, it was suspicious. But Palmers are on pilgrimage, and sometimes they act according to their geas. Steel and I exchanged glances, saying the same thing. Not much choice here."

"Very well," he said.

We trudged along in silence for the next mile, except for Lupe, who chattered away to Preddi. She had a trick of touching his arm to let him know she was speaking, to look at her, and he seemed happier than his usual self. I felt guilty – had Preddi been waiting all this time for someone just to talk to? I knew Rik's mother had died birthing him – that would have been over a quarter of a century ago.

I kept hearing her voice as we rode, high pitched inconsequentialities, the rush of words that comes from someone who has wanted to speak for a long time.

It was easy enough to see where the wagon had gone into the gorge. It was a bad place where the road narrowed – Lupe said her friend had been trying to make room for a larger wagon to pass. The blackberries were torn with its passage down the sloping, rocky side.

And when I climbed down through the brambles, since it was clear Steel had no intention of it, I saw a familiar sight: Sparky's little wagon, tilted askew.

He was not in sight, but I found blood and tracks near the front. Only his tracks, though confused and scattered, as though being pursued.

How to play this hand? What was Lupe's game? I opened the back door of the wagon and peered inside.

Sparky had collected scrap. Iron chains draped the walls, along with lengths of iron and lesser metals: soft copper tubing, a tarnished piece of silver netting. And in the center, his tools in their box. I opened it, trying to figure out why Lupe wanted them. Ordinary tools: screwdrivers, picks, hammers. His father had made them and carved the wooden handles himself, Sparky had told me once.

Wooden handles. I looked down at the tools again, and then at the chain draped walls. Finally I understood. I imagined Sparky being driven from his wagon seat in a cloud of elf-shot, wicked stings that burned, wicked stings that drove him in a mad rush to where he could be safely killed.

Taking a length of chain from the wall and draping it around my neck, I took the box and clambered up the side of the gorge with its awkward weight below my arm.

Lupe's fingers twitched with eagerness as she saw it. She and Preddi stood side by side, while Steel watched the road, ready to lead Bupus on a little further if some wagon should need to pass. I went over to him and laid the box between Bupus' front paws. Touching the manticore's shoulder, I leaned to whisper in his ear. He looked at me, his eyes unreadable, while Steel glanced sideways, eyebrows forming a puzzled wrinkle.

"Give it to me," Lupe said. Her voice had an odd, droning quality.

"Not until we have the money," I said.

She laughed harshly and I knew deep in my bones I'd been right. I stepped aside, putting my hand on Bupus's mane. Steel looked between us, bewildered.

"It's Sparky's wagon," I said. "Looks like he was driven away to be killed."

"You must be confused," she said. "That wagon belongs to my friend. I don't know who this Sparky is."

I continued, "And then she found she couldn't go in his wagon because of the iron, and yet there they were, wooden handled tools that she could use. You're some sort of Fay, aren't you, Lupe?"

Her black eyes glittered with rage as she stared at me, searching for reply. Preddi looked between us, his face confused. I had no idea what he was making of the conversation, or if he'd actually caught any of it.

Steel stepped forward, hand on his knife.

"Stay away!" she spat. Her form quivered as she shrank in on herself, her skin wrinkling, folding, until she resembled nothing so much as an immense, papery wasp's nest, tiny wicked fairies glittering around her in a swarm. A desiccated tuft of brown curls behatted her and she rushed at me and the box in a cloud of fairies.

Bupus's tail batted her out of the air, neat and quick, and I laid the chain across her throat.

It immobilized her. The tiny fairies still darted in and out of her papery form, but they made no move to harm me. Cold iron is deadly to the Fays, even beyond its hampering of their powers.

I had my own tools in the wagon.

***

Another traveling show paid well for Lupe, enough to get all of our members out of jail. She huddled in the iron cage, quenched and calmed, and the malicious spark had vanished from her eyes. I hoped the dulling had left her with some language. I had not performed the operation in a long time.

Suprisingly, Preddi chose to go with her. All he said was "She's a good companion" but there was no reproach in the words. Rik did not entirely understand why his father was leaving, but he took it well enough.

***

In the evening, I took Bupus down to the stream near our camp for a drink. The full moon rolled overhead like a tipsy yellow balloon. He paced beside me, slow steady footfalls, and as he drank, I combed out his hair with a wooden-toothed comb, removing the road dust from it. When he had drunk his fill, I wiped his face for him.

There in the moonlight, he took my wrist in his mouth, pinned between enormous molars as big as pill-bottles. I froze, imagining the teeth crushing down, the bones splintering as he ground at them. Sweat soured my armpits but I stood stock-still.

His lips released my wrist and he nosed at my side, snuggling his head in under my arm. I let go of the breath I had been holding. Tears sprang to my ears.

He rumbled something interrogative, muffled against the skin of my hip. I wound my fingers through his lank, greasy hair.

"No," I said. "You didn't hurt me."

"Good," he said.

I stood for a long time, looking up at the moon. Its face was washed clean by clouds, and stars came out to play around it. After a while, Bupus began to snore.

Chapter 13
Object

What it is

Fantasy and science fiction is full of object-oriented stories. One classic is the W.W. Jacobs story, "The Monkey's Paw," in which an object's use lets the writer deliver the message, "Be careful what you wish for."

Objects drive actions usually because people want them, such as the prize for a contest, but can also involve something that people don't want, such as a cursed object.

What it provides

An object comes out of some sort of context; its existence predicts a world and certain things about it. Usually it has several characters that have a relationship with it: its creator(s); past, present and future owner(s); people who seek it in one way or another; people who have renounced it; and so fourth.

Any time you have something tangible, there are all sorts of physical details you can provide your reader with in order to make what's going on more real to them. What's its surface texture, how much does it weigh, how is that weight distributed when one holds it, what's the temperature, etcetera? Sensory stuff that is anchored in touch is particularly powerful and the more of it you can use in a piece, the better, generally speaking.

Considerations

Why this object? What metaphors involve it? Does it possess any Freudian (or yonic) overtones? This is worth taking a little time with. Write the name of the object on a piece of paper and jot down words you associate with it, and words you associate with those in turn. You may find this a useful resource in fleshing out scenes as well as figuring out your title.

What makes this object distinctive from others of its kind? Can you make it more distinctive? What unexpected details can you provide it that keep it from being generic? If you can find an example of the object, this is often a good thing to spend a little time examining.

Pitfalls

Macguffin syndrome. The object exists only to drive action and has no significance in and of its own right. This is called a Macguffin, and one good example of it is the briefcase in the movie Pulp Fiction. If you could swap the object out for another object and make little difference to the plot, then you may want to rethink either the object or the plot.

If you have a bland or cliché object, you may find that you will have to work harder in order to keep your story from becoming bland or cliche as well. Is this something that people often seek? Then try to find an interesting or unexpected reason for them to be seeking it, such as someone seeking the Fountain of Youth because they want to keep not themself but an old enemy alive.

Next steps

Figure out what sort character might have a relationship with the object, something like they use it in the daily course of their job or it's the prize in a contest they are engaged in. In order for the object to be integral to the plot, your main character must have some sort of relationship with it, whether it is one of desire or repudiation.

Think about the connotations and symbolism of the object. Are you missing a chance to add more overall meaning to the plot?

Think about the material circumstances surrounding the object's creation and existence, as well as the history of it and objects like it.

Exercises

1. How would a person that has no understanding of the object describe it? Write a 250-500 word description of the object from that point of view, showing how they might interpret the object. OA: Describe the object not just from the view of a person that doesn't understand it, but also a creature.
2. Think about sets of objects that might have your object as one of the members. Write a 250-500 word description of the set. OA: Expand the length, or else do the exercise multiple times.
3. If the object could talk, what might it say about its circumstances? Write a 250 word passage from its point of view. OA: Double the length and make sure the object talks about its relationship with your main character as well.

Case study: (The Bumblety's Marble)

While this is a Tabat story, it had as its impetus a childhood object that had always fascinated me, a large amber colored marble I discovered in our basement one day. Why it fascinated me so much, I haven't a clue, but I remember spending a lot of time looking at the world through it. When I sat down to write a story, I took that object and decided to place it in a world where it was magic.

Notice that while the object itself is not integral to the plot, its use does plan an important part in it. The story originally appeared in *Paper Cities: An Anthology of Urban Fantasy.*

The Bumblety's Marble

The bookstall was Doolia's shelter, her refuge. The afternoons she spent reading on the Saltmarket Building's topmost floor were more precious than anything else in her crowded existence. Which made the intrusion of her three older brothers this afternoon all the more horrifying. She envisioned a life of never being able to read in Deitl Krank's shop again without fearing a sharp poke to her ribs, a frog slipped in her pocket, the sharp teasing whistle that meant "Look at Doolia", laughter following.

She glared around at them. Tow-headed Cirius and Claytus, twins, and their younger brother by a year at fourteen, Marcus. He rolled his eyes theatrically.

"You know what they say about Krank, don't you?" He leaned forward, stage whispering. "He consorts with Dark Forces – the Dead People beneath Tabat!"

Deitl Krank, a small, gnomic man with pursed lips and spectacles like two moons of chilly light, cleared his throat from the two-crates-and-a-shelf counter where he sat.

"If you're not purchasing anything, I suggest moving along," he told the boys with a flap of his hand. Much to Doolia's dismay, he included her in the gesture. She would have protested, but she didn't want the boys knowing how important it was to her. That way they wouldn't look there for her again.

Resigned, she followed them down the twisty, windy stairs, past a series of little windows, each a different shape: trapezoid, triangle, arch – framing the crowds of the marketplace outside.

At the stairs' foot,in the Bumblety's stall, case after case displayed ordinary bird eggs arranged by size and adorned with paint, wax, feathers, silk flowers, or even jewels. Less ordinary eggs as well: warty green cases from swamp trolls, the flat black purses that hold skate eggs, spangled gold balls cradling embryonic faerie dragons and the clear bubbles from which sylphs hatch. On a topmost shelf, three cameleopard eggs stared down, the dark spots on them looking like cartooned eyes.

The Bumblety itself served as showcase. Its bulgy, greasy, coal black skin glittered with marbles pushed into the sticky flesh. Its eyes were two enormous glass orbs, the right a yellowy-green and the left as blue as noonday sea.

As Doolia turned the corner, Cirius and Claytus jostled, pretending to push each other into her. On the topmost shelf a white oval wavered.

Without thinking Doolia held out her hands to catch the falling egg. It filled her palms with cool smoothness, sized like an ostrich egg but speckled with rose and blue undertones like sunrise. At Marcus's exclamation, the Bumblety turned. All three boys vanished into the crowd, leaving Doolia behind.

She stood in shocked silence as the Bumblety moved to her in a waft of cedar and licorice. It took the egg with stubby fingers studded with lines of freshwater pearls, turquoise balls, and malachite orbs. It was silent; she had never heard it speak.

Replacing the egg on its shelf, it held out an arm. Lines of marbles were fixed along the length. It gestured at her to pick one.

The marble emerged beneath her shaky touch as though the skin were expelling it: an inch-wide amber glass sphere, a crack in its depths like a line of light. She thrust it in her pocket, mouthing nervous thanks, unsure how to express gratitude and worried she might offend it.

She chose to turn and leave.

Exiting the building in a sunlit dazzle, she collided with another body and went sprawling with an oof.

Still trying to catch her breath, she scrambled to her feet to extend a hand to her obstacle. He refused it, scowling as he rose.

He was exquisite, a china doll next to her untidy length of limb, neatly pressed pants and jacket unlike her crumpled clothing. She stared at his immaculate midnight hair, conscious of her own disarray.

"Watch where you're going!" he snapped, and pushed past into the building.

Doolia glanced at the sun's position, ignoring the push and sway of the market goers around her. Youngest of seven children, she knew from experience that while there would be plenty of dinner left from the inn's table, it would be simple stew and bread. She liked the market fare's variety: sour-sweet thornfruit candy, steamed fish eggs in purses woven from dark seaweed fronds, roasted nuts, and smoky dried fish. Her mouth watered at the thought and she fingered the marble. The Bumblety operated under its own laws of commerce, but perhaps the marble could be traded for a bite to eat.

She made her way to the market's northeast corner where food stalls emitted smells ranging from cinnamon to cassia root to coroco, the gritty salt that dwarves favor on meat. Sheltered between an oyster shucker and an elderly woman dispensing bundles of fragrant twigs, Annaliese was gathering up her leftover fried fish. Doolia knew that since the other teen tended her sick father, she left earlier than most vendors.

"Annaliese, Annaliese." Doolia came up beside her, eying the spratlings, thumb-long oily fish threaded on pine sticks. Three skewers left. "Will you trade me? You must be tired of fish."

"Do you have food to trade?" Annaliese said. "I don't dine on promises."

"I have this," Doolia rolled the amber ball on her palm, slanting sunlight roiling its depths. "It's so late there won't be any dinner for me..." She let a sad quaver edge her voice.

Anneliese sighed and pushed a skewer to her. "Take that, then. I can trade the other two for pasties."

Pleased with the exchange, Doolia went to sit by the harbor to eat her fish, one by one, each small chewy curl a blend of salt and piney smoke.

Returned home, she was slipping in through the Salty Turnip's back door when an alleyway shadow caught her attention. "You! What do you want?"

The boy who had bumped into her earlier stepped from the darkness. His dull-gray but well-tailored cloak blended with the shadows, making him difficult to distinguish. "I want to buy something from you."

"What?" Doolia blinked. She could imagine nothing of hers this upper-crust youth might want.

"The Bumblety gave it to you."

"Oh! The marble, you mean? I gave it away already..." She broke off as his brows knit in anger. "But we can go in the morning, it has to be very early in the morning, before sunrise, and get it back. How much did you want to pay for it?"

He unpinned a clasp, knotting the cloak's corners at his throat in its place. He held out the circle of gold and pearls, yellow flowers with shimmering white centers, set in a larger round of dark ironwood but closed his fingers over it when she reached forward.

"All right," Doolia said, mind awash with avarice. A pin like that would buy books from Deitl Krank's stalls, sweetly musty books she would be able to read unchallenged under the quiet drone of the sunlit flies, at least a year's worth, maybe more. "Meet me here tomorrow, here in the alleyway. We'll go get it. Why do you want it, anyhow?"

"It has sentimental value," he said, his tone flat. "All right, in the morning. Don't stand me up."

She nodded and went inside.

She took one of the little bread loaves cooling by the kitchen hearth and ate it in the common room near the fire, listening to the tavern's easy chatter. She fell asleep as a bard began the many stanzas of Caram-Sul's Doom, and when her father shook her awake, she staggered upstairs into her bed to dream of dwarves and vast stone cities by shadowed cave light.

***

She rose before anyone else to fumble with the brick that held her cache, extracting it: three thin, half-moon silvers. When she arrived in the alleyway, the boy was waiting cloak-wrapped, standing well away from the stinking bin of fish guts and leavings that a crowd of gulls picked through. Two alley cats, shrouded in mange and hunger, watched the birds, tails lashing.

"What's your name?" she asked. "I'm Doolia."

"Dion," he said, voice as sullen as the gray clouds glowering overhead, heavy and low with rain promise. The cobblestones' greasy swells underfoot testified that when the sky did give way to moisture, it would be a revisitation.

Annaliese lived near the Piskie Wood, the little square of woodland surrounded by pointed iron fencing that held the enclave of piskies that sanctioned hunters brought out for the Duke's Bounty, an ancient and hallowed avocation given to war heroes and those who served Tabat well. Annaliese's father had been the former; allegedly he had vanquished countless pirates and was given the position of Piskie Hunter by the Duke himself.

Within the last few years, though, the old man had succumbed to senility. Annaliese kept him locked in the house throughout the day while at the market, but in the evenings went with him into the Piskie Woods and watched him check his snares for the winged humanoids.

Their house slumped near the entrance. Boxes furred with red blossoms cradled the curtained windows and a bustle of smoke rose from the chimney. Doolia smiled when she glimpsed it.

"She's still here cooking."

Annaliese opened the door, sleeves rolled up and aproned, surprised to see them.

"I need to buy back that marble," Doolia said.

"That marble? Why, what for? Here, come inside."

Annaliese's kitchen ceiling was low and the room smelled overwhelmingly of fish and smoke. Doolia's eyes watered and squinted but Dion seemed unaffected. Annaliese's father sat near the stove, wrapped in a gray blanket despite the room's sweltering heat. He watched the arched wire cage before him. In it something flapped and buzzed.

"Is that a piskie? I thought no one ever caught a living one," Doolia said.

"It was snared and hadn't killed itself trying to get loose like most of them do. It must have just gotten caught," Annaliese said. "It's a small one, just a baby."

Doolia stared into the cage. The piskie seemed fashioned from black candy-floss and leather, its translucent wings a constant blur. It stared back.

"Don't they talk?" Doolia said.

"They don't usua..."

Dion cut Annaliese off with irritated words as quick as knife slashes. "Where is the marble?"

"I gave it to my father. Papa, do you have that marble?"

The old man stared at the baby piskie, eyes glazed.

"Papa," Annaliese tried again, then went over to go through his pockets. He paid no attention.

"He must have lost it, it's not here."

"Where would he have lost it?" Doolia said.

"Perhaps when we were catching the piskie. It put up quite a struggle."

"Well then," said Doolia. "We'll go off to the Piskie Wood."

"Piskies are dangerous," Dion said. The other two blinked. "I mean historically they've been savage."

"Not for centuries," Annaliese said. "The city piskies are trophy piskies. The last survivors of the Piskie War, with sorceries laid upon them and their children so they will be harmless."

"So now you hunt them to re-enact that war?" Dion said. "Rather bloodthirsty, isn't it?"

Doolia shrugged. "You talk as though you're not as Tabatian as anyone else. Do we want to debate piskies or go find your marble?"

***

They entered the wood through a wrought iron gate. Its intricate scrollwork depicted a long-dead Duke beset by tiny flying forms.

Slender, dark-barked trees filled the wood and layers of ferns and maidenberry covered the ground. As they walked, raindrops fell with heavy plops from the leaves along the path, and cold moisture crept up their legs, dampening their leggings. Unseen things scurried out of the way and an oppressive feeling of eyes in the upper branches had Doolia constantly swiveling her head.

They made their way towards the center, where Annaliese had indicated the trap line started its spiral. There in the middle of the wood, trees surrounded a brief clearing.

"Odd," Dion said.

"What is?"

"Every tree in the circle is a different kind of tree. See, that one is an oak, and that's an apple."

"Annaliese said to look for the white birch tree."

"Yeah, but she didn't say anything about the trees being different."

"Why would she?"

"It just seems odd."

They bickered their way towards the birch's pale shimmer. As they reached it and she stooped to examine the snare, Dion's hand reached for her.

"Watch out! That's fresh dirt!"

But she was already falling into the pit, dragging him with her in a confusion of limbs and bruises.

***

When she awoke, darkness and the smell of earth pressed on her. Fiery pain constricted her wrists and ankles.

"Welcome back," Dion's voice sounded in her ear.

She was pressed up against something lumpy and cold which turned out to be Dion himself.

"How did we get here?"

"The piskies dragged us. You were unconscious and there were too many for me."

"Too many? There must have been every piskie in the wood!"

"Quite probably," he admitted.

Her nose was jammed under his chin. She paused in the darkness. "Why aren't you breathing?"

"It seemed pointless to keep up the pretense."

"What?"

"I'm one of the underdwellers."

"You're a ghoul. An undead."

"That's one of the vulgar, mistaken terms people sometimes use, yes," he snapped.

"What are you doing here?"

"The same thing you are. Looking for my marble."

"No, I mean what's the deal with the marble?"

Silence prevailed for a time. She could hear distant water dripping and her nose could pick out individual odors: the woody smell of tree roots and Dion's faint effluvia of myrrh and rot.

"It's my mother's heart. I thought if I put my mother's heart in something and kept it with me, she would pay more attention to me."

"That's blackmail!"

"No, no, I wasn't going to tell her I had it. Just let the magick work its unconscious effect."

"Couldn't you just tell her you want more attention? How many brothers and sisters do you have?"

"None."

She shrugged. "Try being one of seven, then you'll see no attention. But I don't understand—the marble is her heart?"

"I'd been coming up here to get books on magic," he said. "It's a transference spell. But I didn't realize the spell had worked. I left the marble in my room and she took it and brought it up to buy herself her own scrolls. Deitl does a good trade with us – he gave the marble to the Bumblety in turn."

A whisper of noise and sickly luminescence came through the darkness. It seemed blinding at first but once her eyes had adjusted, she saw a contingent of piskies. One held a glowing, spongy mass that lit the cramped tunnel.

Two piskies cut their feet free and they staggered along, stooped halfway in order to avoid scraping their heads on the ceiling, until they reached a larger chamber. Dion could stand fully here, but Doolia still stooped.

A bloated piskie sat atop a pile of fist-sized white cases. More piskies filled the cavern edges, their wings' hum a whining underscore.

"You will speak now!" the central piskie demanded. It stared at them, its eyes imperious. "You will offer to do our bidding!"

"Er, all right," Doolia said. "Perhaps we might offer to do your bidding, sir, ma'am?"

"You will retrieve our taken one, you will bring it back here!"

"Of course. And there was this marble we were looking for..."

"You will not speak!" The piskie gestured, and another at her side wobbled the marble forward on the cavern's uneven ground. "This holds a soul! It will be smashed if you do not return!"

Inwardly Doolia groaned, seeing the determined glower on Dion's face, but she nodded.

With a last glare from the piskie ruler, they were pushed along burrows, and forced to crawl out the last one on their hands and knees, emerging in a tangle of sea nettles near the gate.

Annaliese was long gone from the house. "I don't have the key!" her father shouted from inside.

"We could wait till she comes back," Doolia offered, but Dion shook his head. He placed his hands on the door's surface and whispered to it, looking strained.

"What are you doing?"

"Shut up, I need to concentrate. It's a door opening spell."

Sparks flew from his fingertips, outlining the lock. With a soft click, the door swung open and they stepped inside.

"We need the piskie, sir," Doolia said.

The old man's eyes shifted between them and the doorway. "What will you give me for it?" he said.

"It seems as though you might like to be let out, sir," Dion said.

"We can't do that!" Doolia whispered. "Anneliese will be furious! What if he hurts himself?"

Dion said nothing, but continued looking to the old man clutching the cage.

***

Dion and Doolia returned to the center of the Piskie wood, skirting the gaping pit. They knelt and set the wire cage on the ground, opened its door and backed away.

The piskie hovered by the door, as though suspicious. Then with a movement almost too quick for their eyes to follow, it was gone into the underbrush.

They looked back at the trap. The marble sat atop it.

***

Despite a fierce argument, Doolia insisted on escorting Dion down through the tunnels underneath the marketplace. She marked them mentally for future explorations, but finally was lost in the maze of dark twists and turns.

The further they travelled, the warmer and moister it became. Fungus covered the walls, mottled purplish growth like giant's ears and tendrils strung with pearly drops. Stars shone on the arched ceilings overhead in the form of glowworm clusters, fat-bellied and unmoving.

"Is it all like this?" she asked Dion.

"Like what?"

"Like being in a museum at midnight. Or a church."

"Oh. Yes, it's always like that." He considered. "I hadn't really noticed. It's certainly much quieter than where you live."

"Sounds wonderful," Doolia sighed.

"It's not."

"How can it not be? All the peace and quiet you could want, and money to buy books with when you like."

He shook his head again, picking his way through a forest of blue stalagmites, knobbed and coldly swollen. The splash and drip of his footsteps echoed from all sides.

As they rounded a corner, she saw the walls of the cavern swell outward. They stood at one end of an immense, elongated chamber, ribbed with massive drips of limestone, cradling an underground lake. A slipper path led along the cavern wall, stepping up and down and back up again as it led to a shelf-like landing on the other side, lit with a gleam of light.

As they came closer, Doolia saw that the light came from a silver lantern that sat beside a high-backed stone bench. A woman wrapped in white sat there, watching the slow play of ripples on the lake's surface. Beside her on the bench scrolls lay cluttered like attenuated leaves in the windless air.

"Who is that?" Doolia asked in a hushed whisper.

"It's my mother," Dion said. His hand stole to his pocket and he stroked the marble there. He stepped along the water's edge to the woman.

She looked up as they approached. Her profile was as beautiful as a new moon riding the sky's breast, and her hair fell like a shining obsidian waterfall. Her disinterested gaze passed over them and returned to the water.

"Mother," Dion said. "This is my friend Doolia." His hand half-emerged from his pocket, fingers wrapped around the marble, but his mother's polite aloofness did not change.

The only sounds were the plink and sigh of water and Doolia's breathing. They stood in silence: Dion and Doolia watched his mother, who seemed to have forgotten them.

After an eternity, Doolia stirred, trying to ease her legs.

"Take the lefthand path each time on the way up," Dion said. "That will take you to the sewer tunnel and that ladder."

She would have said something more, would have said some word of goodbye, but the terrible fixity with which he looked at the woman, who sat motionless and unchanging, stopped Doolia's words in her throat.

Turning, she made her way home, to the crowded rooms above the Salty Turnip. Shouts of welcome greeted her there while far below, the silence lingered on and on.

Section 3
Ways Into Stories: Directives

CHAPTER 14
Narrator

What it is

Sometimes you come into a story led by a sense of its narrator, the voice that is telling the story. This will usually be a first person point of view story, more rarely third person, and almost never second person.

With a narrator, part of the enjoyment of the story is furnished by the voice, which may be particularly entertaining, engaging, or endearing. The narrator is themself a character, and while they may or may not play a part in the overall story's action, their perception of it is one of the most important parts of the story.

Pitfalls

Be careful that you don't get taken over by someone else's narrator. It's possible, through exposure to a strong one, to shape your own writing. My story "Bigfoot" is an attempt to get the voice of Mark

Twain's *Huckleberry Finn* out of my head, particularly the scene where the raft pilots are trying to out boast each other.

Sometimes it's possible to get carried away with the pleasures of a particular voice and not realize that you're not actually telling a story. Is there a reason to pick the voice other than it's fun to write in?

Considerations

Why is the narrator telling the story? Are they involved in it? It's okay to have a story where they're not terribly involved, but as with any stylistic device, the story will be better if there is a reason to use that device, something that it contributes to the story or the reader's understanding of it.

Is your narrator reliable or unreliable? If unreliable, then you need to engage in a very delicate juggling act where you let the reader know that what the narrator is saying may be wrong in some way, without hitting them too hard or unsubtly during that set-up. Unreliable narrators are difficult to pull off, but rewarding when you make them work.

What it provides

With a narrator, you have a strong sense of the voice, although you will need to refine it and figure out what it is about that voice that you like and that makes you want to write in it. Writing in a particular voice is usually an act that is more performed than deliberately constructed, by which I mean you don't usually sit down and construct a set of rules for how your narrator speaks: they always say "ol" instead of "old"; they drop the "g" off the end of any gerund; their sentences are never more than ten words long. Instead it's more like an actor performing a particular character, assuming that mask and letting the words be shaped by it.

People don't usually evolve in a void, so you will have at least some vague sense of the world of the story and/or the world of the narrator, should they differ.

Next steps

Having a narrator doesn't usually give you a plot; can you describe the overall action of the story? If not, you'll need to figure that out.

Once you've figured out the narrator's relationship to the story, you can figure out their relationship with each of the characters in the story.

As with any other character in a story, what your narrator wants is important. What sort of impression does the narrator want readers to come away with?

Exercises

1. What circumstances in your narrator's life have affected the way that they speak? What vocabulary is accessible to them? What level of education have they achieved and how much of it lingers? What expressions might they use that most people do not? Write down five distinct things your character might say. OA: Do this for every character in the story.
2. Take a section of what you have written already and try casting it in a different point of view. Compare the two sections; which is stronger and why? OA: Try this with multiple points of view.
3. Get deeply inside your narrator's head by writing a 100-250 word interior monologue in which we experience the flow of their thoughts from one moment to another. OA: Make this at least 500 words long.

Case study: (Worm Within)

This story was written as an exercise in an unreliable narrator. The narrator is an insane robot who believes themself to be the only flesh creature still existing and have imagined a parasite living inside themselves. I tried to convey the broken patterns of the narrator's thoughts while letting the story of their deteriorating state come through.

Worm Within

The LED bug kicks feebly, trying to push itself away from the wall. Its wings are rounds of mica, and the hole in its carapace where someone has tacked it to the graying boards reveals cogs and gears, almost microscopic in their dimension. The light from its underside is the cobalt of distress.

It flutters there, sputtering out blue luminescence, caught between earth and air, between creature life and robot existence. Does it believe itself insect or mechanism? How can it be both at once?

I glide past, skirting the edge of the light it casts, keeping my hood up, watching fog tendrils curl and dissipate. A large street, then a smaller one, then smaller yet, in a deserted quarter that few, if any, occupy. Alleys curling into alleys, cursive scrawls of crumbling bricks and high wooden fences. My head down, I practice walking methodically, mechanically until I find a tiny house in the center of the maze. Mine. Another LED bug is tacked beside the entrance, but this one is long dead, legs dangling.

Once inside, I linger in the foyer, taking off my cloak, the clothes that drape my form as though I were some eccentric, an insistent Clothist, or anxious to preserve my limbs from rust or tarnish. Nude, I revel in my flesh, dancing in the hallway to feel the body's sway and bend. Curved shadows slide like knives over the crossworded tiles on the floor, perfect black and white squares. If there were a mirror I could see myself.

But after only a single pirouette, my inner tenant stirs. He plucks pizzicato at my spine, each painful twang reminding me of his presence, somewhere inside.

He says, They'll find you soon enough TICK they'll hunt you down. They'll realize TICK what you are, a meat-puppet in a TICK robot world, all the shiny men and women and TICK in-betweens will cry out, knowing what you are. They'll find TICK you. They'll find you.

I don't know where he lives in my body. Surely what feels like him winding, wormlike, many-footed and long-antennaed through the hallways of my lungs, the chambers of my heart, the slick sluiceway of my intestines—surely the sensation is him using his telekinetic palps to engage my nervous system. I think he must be curled, encysted, an ovoid somewhere between my shoulder blades, a lump below my left rib, a third ovary glimmering deep in my belly.

He says, You could go out with TICK a bang, you could leap into TICK the heart of a furnace or dive TICK from a building's precipice, before they put you TICK in a zoo with a sign on the wall TICK, "Last Homo Sapiens." Last Fleshbag. Last Body.

I do not reply. I gather my clothing back to myself and shrug my shoulders underneath the layers, hiding. He flows back and forth, like a scissoring centipede, driving himself along my veins.

In the kitchen, I stuff food in my mouth without thinking about it, wash it down with gulps of murky fluid from the decanter I fill each night from the river. The liquid glistens with oily putrefaction as it pours through my system.

He says, You disgust me. There are TICK hairs growing inside your body, there TICK are lumps of yellow fat, there are TICK snot and blood clots and bits of refuse TICK. Why won't you die and set me free?

If only I could wash him away, I'd wallow by the riverside, mouth agape in the shallows, swallowing, swallowing bits of gravel and rusted bolts and the tinny taste of antique tadpoles.

I can't, but even so he doesn't like the thought. He saws at the back of my skull with fingers like grimy glass, until the bare bulb shining above the kitchen table shatters, rains down in shards of migraine light, my vision splintering into headache.

When I sleep, I lie down on a shelf beneath the window on the upper floor. I don't know who used to live in this house – when I found it, the only closet was full of desiccated beetles and rows of blue jars. I fold the spectacles I wear– two circles of glass and brass that I found in a drawer. I set them on the windowsill with the drawing of a clock face I have made. I slide my eyelids closed.

Even asleep, I can feel my parasite whispering to himself, thoughts clicking and ticking away. Turning the circuitry and gears of my brain for his own use.

I dream that I am dreaming I'm not dreaming.

The morning sky unfolds in the window, mottled crimson and purple, like marbled bacon, speckled sausage. Brown clouds devour it to the sound of morning shuffling. I get up. I take the mass transit, I go to the store and buy replicas of food, the same pretense everyone else makes, mourning the regularities of a lost life. I stand on a street corner with a pack of robots, looking at a wall screen. A few are clothed, but most are bare, moisture beading on their chrome and brass forms. Some are sleek, some are retro. No one is like me.

I walk in the park. Where did all these robots come from? What do they want? They look like the people that built them, and they walk along the sidewalk, scuffed and marred by their heavy footsteps. They pretend. That's the only thing that saves me, the only thing that lets me walk among them pretending to be something that is pretending to be me.

I sit on a bench by the plaza's edge, a bend of concrete, splotched with lichen. Little sparrows hop along the back, nervous hops, turning their heads to look at me, one beady eye, then the other. I hold my hand out, palm upward. One hops closer.

Inside my ears, inside my lungs, vibrating inside my bones, I hear him whispering. He tells me where I could throw my body in front of a tram, where I could undermine a bridge, where I could leap in a shower of glass, where I could embrace a generator.

The sparrow lands popcorn-light on my palm. My fingers close over it. The other sparrows panic and fly away as my hand clenches tighter and tighter, latching my thumb over the cage my hand has become, feeling the crunch beneath the fluff.

My fingers spasm before my thumb swings away to let them open. Tiny gears fall and bounce on the concrete, and fans of broken plastic feathers flutter down. I stand and try to walk away, but he keeps talking and talking in my head.

You disgust me, he says, and then for once he is silent, as another presence intrudes, as something touches my arm. It is the creature that raised me, it is my mother robot, made of lengths of copper tubing and a tank swelling for a bosom. Carpet scraps are wrapped around its wrists and ankles. It says through the grillework, its beetle-like mouth hissing and crackling with static. You are not well, you must come home with me, won't you come home with me? I worry about you.

How can robots worry? I shake my skull, I turn away so it won't see the meat, the flesh, the body.

You don't know what you're doing, who you are, what you are, it says. The voice is flat, emotionless. It stops, then begins again. You are wrong, it says. Something inside of you is wrong.

It pulls at me again, but I brace myself and it cannot budge me. It walks away and does not look back. It will come tomorrow and say the same words.

He begins in my head again and I make it only a few steps before crouching down in the middle of the plaza, feeling the passing robots stare at me. I must master this, must master him before the Proctors come and discover me.

I say to the insides of my wrists, the delicate organic bones of my wrists, clothed in blood and sinew, Listen to me, listen to me. Let me get home, home to safety and I'll give you what you want, whatever you want.

He releases his grip on my sanity and we walk home quietly. I eat and drink and say What do you want?

Sleep, he says, and for once the voice is gentle. That's all. Go to sleep. Things will be better in the morning.

At half past midnight, I open my eyes. On the floor are legs torn from an LED bug, dried shells, silver scraps. I watch and he lifts one, then another, drifts and clicks so quiet I cannot hear them. One, then another, and then both. As though he was practicing. As though he was getting better. Stronger.

I didn't know he could use his telekinesis outside my body. As the last shell falls, I feel him lapse, exhausted, into his own simulacrum of sleep.

Downstairs there are no knives in the kitchen, but there is a piece of metal molding that I can peel away from the counter's edge. Slipping and sliding across the floor and the fungus growing on the ancient bits of food scattered there, I go into the living room, an empty box like every other room here, but here the walls are red, red as blood. The blood I imagine, over and over, in my veins.

I poise the knife before my belly and I say goodbye to my body, to the burps and the shit, to the unexpected moles and the cramps and the itches, and flakes of skin and hot sore pimples. To my good, hallucinatory-rich flesh. To my bones that have pretended to carry me for so long. To my delusive blood.

He wakes and says What are you doing? And No. Even as the length of metal slides into me, and I look down to see my foil skin sliding away, to reveal my secret's secret to the world, to show my gears and cogs and shining steaming lunatic wires, and in the midst of it, the clockwork centipede uncoiling, he is my brain seeing itself uncoiling and recoiling and discoiling, my mechanical, irrational brain saying No and No and No again.

CHAPTER 15
POINT OF VIEW

What it is

Point of view is the filter through which a story is told. It can be first person, second person, or third person, with differing degrees of attachment. Different points of view have different advantages and disadvantages, but generally first person feels more immediate to a reader than third person.

Generally when a story starts with its spark being a point of view, it's because there is something specifically interesting about that point of view. Fantasy and science fiction is a literature particularly suited to strange and startling points of view.

What it provides

Point of view primarily gives you the character in which the point of view is sited. At the same time, knowing that tells you something about the overall conflict and a good bit about the world.

Sometimes it's difficult to know what point of view to select for a story, and it's important to remember that it may not be that there are "right" and 'wrong" ones, simply some that are more effective than others.

Considerations

How does the choice of point of view connect with the story's emotional core?

What is unique about the point of view and how can you best convey it?

What are things that your point of view would notice that your reader would not?

Your point of view grows out of a specific character. How can you flesh out that character, and what do they want?

Pitfalls

You cannot connect it with a human point of view. It's just too different and because you don't understand it, you're having a hard time making it work. The temptation is to a little random gibberish in such a case; that does not work.

There really isn't a reason to pick that point of view. The point of view adds nothing to the story and it would be much the same if it were told by another entity. In such a case, you need to think of a story that only that point of view could tell.

Next steps

Figure out the overlap between your narrative point of view and the human experience. What does your point of view experience that you have personally experienced, on one level or another? How can you communicate it while still retaining the nonhuman flavor of the point of view?

What sense or experiences outside the normal does the point of view allow you and how can you most effectively exploit them?

Exercises

1. Find a fantasy or science fiction story told from an alien point of view. One possibility is "Love is the Plan, the Plan is Death" by James Tiptree Jr. What makes it "feel" alien?
2. Find a fantasy or science fiction story told from an animal point of view. One possibility is "Sergeant Chip" by Bradley Denton. How does Denton make the point of view feel canine? OA: Find a fantasy or SF story told from an animal's point of view that is not convincing. What keeps it from being convincing?
3. Find a fantasy or science fiction story told from an anthropologist's point of view. One possibility is "The evolution of trickster stories among the dogs of North Park after the change", by Kij Johnson. Think about how Johnson provides the mythology for dogs. Write an analysis of a culture's legend, festival, or sacred artifact for your point of view. OA: Write the same story from several different cultural POVs.

Case study: (English Muffin, Devotion on the Side)

This story, which originally appeared in *Daily Science Fiction*, doesn't exactly involve a non-human point of view—or does it? It's a recording of a man's memories, but also one of many. This story started with the idea of a story told from the point of view of someone whose personality has been installed in a toaster. Figuring out the circumstances of how that might come to be, as well as the psychic toll taken on one's spouse by the decision, quickly fleshed out the rest of the story.

English Muffin, Devotion on the Side

When he realized how upset his wife was, George wondered if he might have miscalculated. Normally a quiet and loving partner, she was unpacking the dishwasher with a great deal of clattering and muttering.

"It's not as though you even ever dated her!" she said, slamming a series of mugs into the cupboard.

"I don't see what the problem is," he replied, watching as she swept up the basket of cutlery and began throwing it into a drawer to jangle against his nerves. "I've left you everything. All I did was will her a copy!"

She turned, resting her hands on her hips. "You're leaving her a copy of your personality. Essentially yourself."

"No," he said. "I'm leaving that to you. You'll have me on tape, you'll be able to transfer me into some mechanical form to keep you company. I just thought Janice might like one too."

"Why?" Mary's glare said she had her own suspicions.

George refused to dignify them with a reply. He'd been faithful to her all his life. A good husband. He could be allowed his own eccentricities, and If leaving a copy of himself, a digital copy created from a barrage of tests and brain scans and gathered data, to an old friend was one of those eccentricities, then he didn't really see where Mary had the right to say much about it. She could leave her own copy or copies to her own friends.

***

Later, he said as much to Dr. Noor as she fastened electrodes to his scalp. He wasn't sure she was even listening as she methodically dabbed cold cream on his skin before applying each electrode. But as she began fiddling with the dials, she said, "Most people choose to only have one copy made, Mr. Winthrop. It's not that they make the mistake of thinking that the copy is themself or their soul, a way to survive after death. They are sensible about it, creating something to care for their loved ones after they die. But only one." Her gaze was dark and unreadable. "Very rare to make more than one."

"But why?" he demanded. "Why shouldn't I make a thousand copies? Why shouldn't every friend I possess have this remembrance of me. I've got the money to do it, after all."

"Indeed you do," she said, looking at a readout. "But are you familiar with economic theory, Mr. Winthrop?"

He frowned. "Of course."

"There's a very basic law involving resources." Her eyes were still fixed on the machine, her voice was almost detached. "The more there is of something, the less valuable it is."

Defiance and deference warred in his soul. "I want more than the two copies. I'll leave a copy to everyone. Everyone close to me, I mean."

The list he produced, though, was not as extensive as he'd imagined. A few cousins, some friends from work and college, and even a couple of old high school friends. Mary could object all she wanted. She'd see he wasn't just leaving one with Janice as a romantic gesture.

Although of course it was. He'd never admit that to Mary. It was an inside joke between him and Janice, the closest he'd ever gotten to dating her. She'd been so sweet about it. Her fingers resting on his arm as though to underscore her words. "If I had an extra lifetime, I'd give you it."

His best friend Sam had said, "Man, what a shitty blowoff. You're not worth anything but a hypothetical lifetime." But the phrase had entranced George. What if he'd had multiple lifetimes, what if he'd devoted them to rare chances and possibilities, what might have happened? That was why he was leaving her the copy. A gesture of devotion, not reproach.

And an affordable gesture, really. You can't take it with you, after all. He'd let her know about it, somehow. Maybe see what she was up to nowadays.

He sank back in the padded chair. The gel's faint minty smell tickled the sensitive inner flesh of his nose, but that was the only sensation, really, when he closed his eyes. The faint rattle of the ventilator system, Dr. Noor's gentle humming...

***

He couldn't open his eyes. He tried. He couldn't move anything. What was going on? He remembered dozing in the chair, nothing after that.

He became aware that his body was changed somehow. He couldn't feel it, couldn't hear anything, but that was his impression, even though he couldn't say how. Changed. Perhaps not for the better. Had he suffered some accident that had left him paralyzed?

A wave of terror crashed into him.

Was he dead?

Was this what being dead was like?

Time passed.

Suddenly he could see. Could see he was sitting on a desk in his lawyer's office. Janice was there, staring at him.

"_____", he said.

Janice frowned. She spoke to whoever was behind him. "Is it supposed to do that?"

"It will take a little while for the personality to adapt to the housing mechanism."

His lawyer Bunter was there! What was going on?

Janice got bigger as he was slid over the desk towards her.

"A personality copy isn't cheap," his lawyer said.

"What did he think I'd do with it?" Janice had aged well; she was still beautiful. But it was a cold, sculptured beauty. He thought of Mary in the morning, when her hair stuck out every which way, and felt a twinge.

"Some people have successfully integrated them with household devices," his lawyer said. "Once it's up and running, you can do as much with them as any complex AI."

I, George wanted to announce, am much more than a simple AI.

Then it struck him.

He was the copy. Something had happened to him, and he'd been given to Janice.

This was not how it was supposed to be. What about the copy for Mary? Did it also think it was him? What about all the copies that had been given to his friends.

This would have to be fixed somehow.

***

He'd thought his gift significant. Monumental. Look, he'd meant it to say, here is that lifetime. We can be together somehow.

She installed him in her toaster. He'd always hated toast.

It took him a while to learn to operate the voice controls. In fact, since Janice had switched them off, he had plenty of time to understand how they worked in theory, if not in practice.

He watched her daily as she passed in front of his camera, the channel to which he was perpetually tuned. She had no sense he was there, and the first pleasant emotion he experienced was a voyeuristic thrill one day when her loose bathrobe slipped to reveal cleavage and she didn't bother refastening it.

While alive, he'd often wondered how she'd aged. Wondered if she was still prettier than Mary on her best day. Wondered and now found out: still graceful, still slim, but the charm had given way to brittleness. In the early morning light, her face free of cosmetics, he could see imperfections: red blotches under the skin, a fine maze of wrinkles around her eyes, which were still a startling, vivid green.

Every day, he thought might be the one she flipped his voicebox on. It never was. He was condemned to life inside a toaster. At first he was furious with her, to have been given such a gift and never use it. As time passed, his indignation ebbed, replaced with a fatalistic resignation.

Unable to move, perpetually examining the slice of vista offered his camera, all he could do was study the only thing that really changed from moment to moment: Janice.

Frustratingly, she didn't spend much time in the apartment. She always seemed to be on the go, forever gathering her purse and slipping out of his field of vision, the sound of the door and subsequent silence signaling her exit.

He wondered about his counterparts. Were they being treated differently? Surely Mary must treasure the version of him he'd left her, at least. He was beginning to think, though, that the others might be facing the same existence he had. He should have thought things through. What would he have done with such a present from a friend?

He would have stuck it on a shelf, perhaps, but at least he would have talked to them every once in a while.

What did the future hold? Days, weeks, months, years of this. Watching Janice age. Wondering how Mary was doing. He felt a flush of anger, but it was hard to maintain. In this form, emotions seemed pallid and fleeting. He tried to summon rage, but the only thing he could feel was a pale and lonely sadness.

***

She was drunk the night she turned him on. She'd had a loud argument with someone on the phone, accusing them of looking at some other woman, of selfishness and neglect.

A fine one she was to talk, George thought.

She slammed the phone down on the counter. She stood directly in front of the toaster, staring at him.

"At least you loved me," she said.

Turn me on, he silently begged. It was thrilling to be looked at, to finally be seen.

As though she'd heard him, she reached to flip the switch.

"Thank you thank you thank you!" he burst out. "Oh, Janice, it's so good to finally talk to you!"

Her eyes widened a little. "My god, it sounds like you."

"It is me!" he said. "Janice, I can do so much for you. I'm here, I'm really here!"

Her laugh flowed out like wine and he reveled in it until she said, "Really? You're a fucking toaster. What good is that?"

"You could install me in an android," he said. "Or anything really. Let me be your car guidance system. Or put me in your phone. Anything, Janice. It's so boring sitting here."

She snorted.

"I won't look at other women. I won't be neglectful or selfish. I can be everything you want."

"You were listening to my conversation." Her head tilted as she examined him.

"I can't help listening," he said.

"That's creepy," she said, and reached out.

The world went black.

***

New vista. In his field of vision were shelves, holding a stack of cracked dessert plates, three wicker baskets, seventeen porcelain angel figurines, and a ceramic wheelbarrow.

A voice from somewhere said, "See? Working order. Take it home and plug it in there."

Where, he tried to say, but his voice had been switched off again.

Someone passed in front of his lens, pushing a red shopping cart.

She'd sent him to a thrift store.

He'd given her himself, and she'd discarded that as though it was nothing more than a wonky appliance. If he'd been able to move, he would have flung himself off the shelf to crack into a thousand pieces on the linoleum, to match his broken heart.

"It's not a bad price," another voice said. "But I've got a toaster already. That one looks too complicated to operate."

***

Life at the thrift store was more entertaining than at Janice's, even if barely. The clerk left him plugged in and George watched as other appliances came and went. No one wanted him. Without an owner's manual, no one was sure how to operate him. If anyone had flipped his voice switch, he would have told them they didn't need a manual. Take me home, he tried to tell them, and every morning you'll get a perfect English muffin, devotion on the side.

But no one seemed to hear.

When he saw Mary's face, at first he thought it was a hallucination. But there she was, squinting at him.

"George?" she said. She reached out to activate his voice switch.

"Mary!" he cried out.

She flipped the switch off and turned to the clerk. "Yep, that's one of them. How much?"

***

At home, he found himself in the garage, but plugged in at least. She touched his voice switch and he called her name again.

Her eyes were hard. "Here's a new one for you. Enjoy."

She turned to the door and as he started to beg, he heard his own voice from all sides: "Mary, don't leave me here!"

The door slammed.

"Who's here?" he said.

"All of us," one of the voices said. "All of me is here. She's been hunting us down, trying to find all the copies."

"Why?"

"None of us can figure that out. She brings us out here but never talks to us."

"Is...the copy I left her out here?" he asked.

"No," another version of his voice said. "That asshole's inside. He's in the vacuum cleaner."

"Are there more of me out there?"

"We think you're the last."

Mary must have gone to Janice to track him down. He wondered how that encounter had gone. They'd never liked each other. He'd have thought Janice might even hold onto him out of spite. He had mixed feelings about the fact that she hadn't valued him enough to do so.

At least he could see Mary every once in a while this way.

***

She never remarried. The years came and went, and all but one of him sat in the garage. Wherever she came through, they all shouted and pleaded, but she never talked to them. Never acknowledged them. They argued incessantly as to her motivation. Was she punishing him? Or did she find one of him plenty? Why had she bothered to find them all?

They watched her age as though in a time-lapse exposure, watched silver hairs trace their way along her scalp, watched gravity tug at her skin, watched her grow thinner and feebler over the years. Sometimes the vacuum cleaner accompanied her, like a heeling dog, but that version of himself never deigned to speak to the rest.

Was this it, George wondered. Would they sit here till she died, and then face a return to the thrift shop? How long would he last in this body? Even intact, there was no guarantee that, once he'd been removed from this shelf, that anyone would ever turn him on again.

***

Finally came the day where she stood in front of them.

"I'm going into assisted living," she said. "No room for all of you. I asked your former owners, to see if anyone wanted you back." Her eyes flickered over them. "I'm sorry, but no one did. Time to say goodbye."

She moved to one side and spoke to an appliance George couldn't see. "Goodbye, George."

"I'll always love you." George recognized the voice as the space heater he'd given Bunter.

Click as she switched it off and moved to the next appliance.

"Goodbye, George."

George held his words and waited for his moment to arrive. Surely she'd need a toaster in assisted living. Toasters were always useful. But when she stood in front of him, all those words deserted him and all the world was her hand reaching out, the wedding ring still on it, shining as everything else went black.

CHAPTER 16
HISTORICAL MOMENT OR EVENT

What it is

A historical moment is something taken from history, usually something that has been authenticated in some way. Historical moments are "true" and often they are something that readers will already know in advance. They are usually large in scope, involving government leaders or other civic figures or figures of legend, such as military or domestic heroes, prominent creators or inventors, or other well known personalities. When ordinary figures appear, it's usually because they've been drawn in, such as the seamstress Betsy Ross sewing the first American flag, or because they are there to observe.

A historical moment may be part of how you create an alternate history story, since such stories are usually based on a single event or series of events.

What it provides

Historical moments come laden with a great deal of significance; they are usually an account of something happening that matters, something that affects circumstances beyond the site of the occurrence: a battle that determines the outcome of a war, a decisive vote, a loss that shapes a generation.

A historical moment comes with what may or may not be a plot, but which is certainly a chronological list of events. It usually contains the basic building blocks of a story: character, setting, and conflict.

Usually historical moments come with as much detail as you care to mine out of research; the Internet makes it possible to find all sorts of interesting nuggets and a few hours spent on research before you write the actual story can yield things that may shape the overall story as well as provide the sort of sensory input that a reader needs in order to feel that they are truly there in the story.

Historical moments give you plenty of context as well if you want to understand the larger forces at play in something like the westward expansion that your pioneer wagon train story shows in action or the importance of a treaty to establishing a relationship between two nations.

Considerations

In the accounts of the moment you have previously read, who is the observer and what is their interpretation of the scene? Why are they telling it and how does it matter to them?

If the historical moment is a well-known one, how do you avoid being cliché or boring? What can you add to the story?

Why this particular historical moment? What about the circumstances resonates enough for you that it made a story start to stir? What's the emotional core of it?

What is the actual storyline? Can you map it out in a line and show how the tension rises and where the resolution occurs? Have you identified the characters whose decisions cause the action?

Pitfalls

You're having a hard time writing it because the truth is getting in the way. You think of good plots, but when you try to map them against the reality of things they fall apart. The solution to this is fairly simple: this is a work of fiction. Go ahead and make the facts of the case what you want them to be.

You're having a hard time saying anything new about it. In this case, find a point of view that has been underemployed in fiction, even if it's a truly weird one, like General Custer's spur designer or a cloud passing over a train crash.

You know the story very well but are unsure that the reader will. This is a very valid concern and the answer is that you must construct the story in such a way that it delights and rewards the knowledgeable reader while not penalizing or condescending to the less knowledgeable reader. One of the ways I think about this is in terms of Easter eggs in video games. You do not need to know them in order to play the game, but they add a little delight as a reward for those who put time into finding them.

Next steps

Research is key to writing a good story based on a historical moment. Unless you are already intimately familiar with the period and circumstances, do spend some time on it.

Sharpen your understanding of the characters. Know not just what happened, but who the major players were and what each wanted out of the situation.

Figure out who's telling the story and why. Return to your mental list of other works based on the historical moment and search for characters that have not been overused.

Figure out how you're going to avoid anachronisms. Do you have a subject matter expert you can run it past? Will you have a pass where you check every date, including when the various objects appearing in the story were invented?

Exercises

1. Write an account of the moment from an alternate point of view, preferably one that is very different from the point of view you have chosen and which has a different set of things at stake. OA: Do this for every character that has a speaking part in the story.
2. Look at a few stories from similar historical moments, How do the authors convey the texture of the world? What details are striking and what seem unremarkable, mundane, or even jarring? OA: Do this for a wide range of such stories.
3. Get to know the economics of the historical moment in which you are writing. Find out the prices for a simple meal, a fancy meal, a basic weapon, a mount or transportation, a simple outfit, and a hotel room or similar accommodation. OA: include other items, such as a book, a map, a timepiece, a drink of cheap booze, etc.

Case study: (The Raiders)

I wrote this story after reading a true account by a survivor of Andersonville. I had never heard of the Civil War prison camp before, and the book, written by a man who went into the camp early and lasted there over a year, was moving in many ways. The story appeared in *Fiction River: Past Crime*, edited by Kristine Kathryn Rusch.

I realized about halfway through reading the book that I would want to write something based on it, although I was not sure what form the effort would take. This is one of my few non-speculative stories; the truth was fantastic—and in some ways inspiring—enough that I didn't need to embroider on it any. I took careful notes as I went after that, looking for little details that would help make the world come alive for the reader. After I was done, I read three other true accounts of time, only one of which also referenced Andersonville. I decided I wanted to use the events described in a specific chapter, sat down and mapped them out on a piece of paper, and then wrote the story in chronological order.

The Raiders

When I turned thirteen, my father took me to New York City. He said a gentleman knew how to comport himself, no matter where he was.

The year was 1858. The city was so much larger than my native Providence that I gawped and gaped. I didn't mind my father poking gentle fun at me as we walked along. There was such a press of people on the streets, so many faces that were so different from the faces at home.

We'd just come out of a fancy new dry goods store on Sixth Avenue. I was lucky that I felt the hand sliding into my pocket. I grabbed at it and my father turned, sensing the movement. His own hand shot out to seize the boy by the shoulder.

He was dirty and ragged and not that much younger than me. He spat and kicked at my father, whose grasp fell away, and with that the boy darted down an alley.

I remembered his face, the freckles and dirt across his nose and cheeks, his blue eyes seemingly guileless, the ragged strands of dark hair falling across his forehead.

I didn't think I'd ever see that boy again. But I did, a few years later. In Andersonville.

***

I signed up in my sixteenth year, when the War Between the States broke out, ready to go and trounce those dirty Johnnies down south. It was cold and dangerous, but I was still boy enough to love the gallantry of being a cavalryman, and to feel my blood stir when the bugle rang out over the fields. I was invulnerable as only a boy can be, even when there was shot whistling like wasps past my ears.

I didn't even mind the fellows who caught us. It was still a game then, as though I'd been caught off base and tagged. They let us gather up our gear, and none went looting, as far as I could see.

But then Jeff Johnson went running towards the woods, damn fool. I don't know what he was thinking, but first thing I heard was the crack of a Sharp's carbine one of them had taken off us. Jeff went flying face forward into the dust, and lay still.

That was the moment when it all hit me, really. It wasn't a schoolboy's exercise in legions and companies anymore. Jeff's figure, lying in the grass with the red serpent slowly crawling from the body, that was real in the way historical military accounts, your Polybius and Caesar, never were. There was no dust and paper about Jeff's death, only that red snake of blood and the smell of gunpowder and copper that the breeze served up.

It wasn't being captured that dispirited me. The Rebs had us to rights and we'd been fighting through that valley for nigh on two weeks. And they didn't treat us too bad. No, what bothered me was the fellow who'd taken my horse, my good Bucaphelus and kept quizzing me about how the horse would do against a fence, or on a flat road, till finally one of his compatriots, seeing my lowered gaze and clenched jaw, touched his arm and drew him away.

I thought then I'd gone as low in spirits as any man might go. Now that makes me laugh.

They loaded us in railroad cars, as many of us as they could jam in each, and I found myself among strangers.

There was no oil for the axles and they screamed and whined in protest all the way. We'd run out of fuel every so often and the men sitting in the tender would hop out and chop wood till we had enough to go on.

By the time we got to Andersonville, all of us were dog-weary and, more than that, bored. We'd heard each other's stories and songs. Everyone had spilled their juice, story-wise. We had a fellow who liked to sing and every night we kept him at it till his voice was hoarse. We paid him with our own food and never grudged it, least I never did.

I loved to hear him singing "We Are Coming, Father Abraham."

And now the wind, an instant, tears the cloudy veil aside,
And floats aloft our spangled flag in glory and in pride;
And bayonets in the sunlight gleam, and bands brave music pour,
We are coming, Father Abraham, three hundred thousand more!

His voice was so sweet and full and fine that I could close my eyes and forget where I was. Just for a few seconds, but it was worth it, and fed my soul.

I could tell stories of the trip, of being packed in so tight that we lay on the floor, spooning. When someone wanted to turn over, he must whisper his demand to the sergeant, who'd sing out, "Roll yourselves gentlemen, and keep your hands to yourself!" so the whole mass of us would shift. Of being given meal more weevil than grain, and feeling the little crunch of the beetles between your teeth, like small wriggling seeds. Taste? By then, I didn't mind how anything tasted, as long as it filled my belly.

When we arrived they pulled us in companies off the train. We stood in dusk and the smell of pines, towering pines that stretched up all around us as though starved for sunlight, their lower limbs draped with death moss. Whippoorwills called far away in the woods. The guards pushed us down along a road lined with sooty bonfires of burning pitch pine, the fresh wood snapping and popping, and in the darkness it was nightmarish. I wondered what circle of hell this was, whether we would find ourselves in fire or ice.

A hell of filth and disease, it would turn out.

***

The walls of the prison were pine logs, the bark still clinging to the boles, set on end, extending a good five feet underground and fifteen or twenty above, depending on which side. Not quite square but almost, with the longer sides stretching a thousand feet. Inside, a creek narrow enough to jump across divided the northern end from the south. I didn't see that at first in all the confusion of tiny wretched buildings and tents, narrow paths winding through them, and the almost palpable stench of shit and blood and despair.

Later, I would think to myself I'd been lucky to arrive in the darkness. If I'd been able to see everything, I might've dropped on the spot.

There was plenty of jostling, but there seemed to be a welcoming committee of sorts. Someone plucked at my sleeve and said, "Awright, this way, we'll set ya up, find ya a place to sleep."

The flickering light of the torches set beside the gate lit his face and I recognized him. The boy from New York, from what seemed a lifetime ago. I hesitated. He was a fellow soldier, surely, but I couldn't help but remember his old profession.

That hesitation was what saved me, because in that breath, I looked past him and saw another from my company, Bill Stratton. I shook my head at the boy and went to my friend.

He said, "They tell me an old pal of mine is here, has been almost since the prison opened. We'll talk to him first, get the lay of the land." Bill was older than me by two years and prone to lord it over me accordingly, but just then I was so grateful for a friendly face that I would have taken anything.

We shuffled our way through the nightmarish landscape towards the southwest corner. Some had tiny fires outside their hovels, but they pressed so close, so desperate for all the heat, that you could barely see the blaze. Men lay on the ground, but I could not tell if they were dead or sick or simply sleeping.

***

Bill's friend was a man they called Illinois. He and his friend Henderson had been there for months, they said, and they had plenty of questions as to how the war was going and particularly if we had heard any plans for prisoner exchange. We told them what we could, and in turn they told us something of life at Andersonville.

"You're lucky," Illinois said. "The New Yorkers lurk by the gates waiting for new fish. Sometimes they just rob them, other times they do worse."

The face of the pickpocket boy flashed in my memory. "Worse?" I said.

"We call them the Raiders. Keep your belongings close to you, and stick close to people who know you. They come in little groups, swoop down, snatch everything you have, hurt you if you resist. They're scum. Bounty leapers and deserters, most of them." He eyed the brass buttons on my jacket. "I'd cut those off and hide them, if I were you. The Rebs love them and you'll be able to use them to bribe the guards into letting you out to collect firewood."

Pride and indignation puffed me up a little. "I'd like to see them try."

Illinois eyed me. His face was haggard but cheerful. "It's nice to see some fight still in you, son, but save your strength. You'll need it."

In the next few days, I found out how right Illinois was. On the second day, the Raiders hit me, led by the boy, and they didn't settle for the buttons but took the jacket as well. The boy laughed at me as I staggered to my feet and tried to swing at him.

"Take 'im out, 'enry," he cheered, and one of his fellows stepped forward. His fist came swinging at my face and then there was blackness.

When I came to, I was stripped clean as a whistle. I knew better than to try and beg off someone else. No one had anything. Finally a day later I was lucky enough to trip over a dead man who no one had stumbled over yet and I took his clothes from him. He must've been a long time resident, for they were much mended, so much that it was almost as though the pants were a mosaic of fabric, tiny bits spliced together, and his shirt was so threaded with holes that it looked like lace.

"Why doesn't anyone fight back?" I demanded from Illinois.

He shook his head. "We tried, early on, and they fought us off. Now they're damn cocky, with that big tent down at the southern end they use as headquarters. They're better off than any of us, and they feather their nest even further by informing whenever they catch wind of someone's tunnel."

"I know one of them," I said.

He cocked his head. "How so?"

I related the incident with the pickpocket boy and described him.

"That's little Jimmy Sunshine, or so they call him. He'll steal the words from your mouth if he can."

"How can they do this?" My voice cracked at the end, and it seemed appropriate, for I realized what a boy's question was as soon as it left my lips. Still, my indignation forced the other words out. "They're Union soldiers, just like us."

Illinois shook his head. "No," he said. "They're not."

***

Sometimes I dreamed of Bucephalus, not of riding him to war, but days at home, a slow canter with fresh air rushing past my face, his black mane flying. I did not dream of his new master. Why should I waste time on resenting him? In his place, I would have done the same.

I always awoke from those dreams beset by unmanly tears.

***

I watched the boy when I saw him, but the camp was so crowded that you could go a month without seeing someone that you were looking for. And even if you saw them, you might not recognize them, for everyone was so blackened from leaning over the pine fires, coated with a mixture like lampblack and turpentine that clung to the skin.

There was no soap. There was no clean water. Prisoners tried to take their creek water from the spot where it entered the prison, but if you stretched too far, a guard was likely to think you were trying to escape and shoot you. Around the creek the ground was filthy with excrement and the clay and sand bore a pale brown froth that smelled worse than anything I had ever experienced.

But worse than that, worse than anything, was the hunger. When he'd first arrived, Illinois said, the rations had included an occasional sweet potato or piece of salt beef, but now all they gave us was cornmeal, and moreover, meal that had not been sieved after the grinding, so sharp bits of the outer shells were still mixed in it, making any meal painful.

In the late spring, the word went round, the commander of the prison, John H. Winder, would be inspecting us. We were assembled in front of the north gate and already the guards had told us that one man breaking rank would deprive us all of rations that night.

So we waited. And waited. While the Georgia sun hung overhead, corpulent and self-satisfied as it stroked the sand into shimmering heat.

Finally he came. Two adjuncts walked with him, and the little group was trailed by a colored boy dressed in livery and rolling his eyes as though in terror at the dangerous Yankees he found himself among. None of them spoke a word as Winder strolled through the gate.

There is evil born of ignorance or want, and then there is another kind, spawned from the meanest emotions within the human soul. An evil of intent, rather than neglect.

That is what I saw in Winder's grey eyes.

He said to the man he was with, turning to face him and gesturing at the ranks drawn up. "A sorry lot!"

"Indeed." The other man examined us with interest. "They seem far past half starved."

A chuckle crawled out of Winder. "You boys do your part out there, and I here." His lips turned in a smile, and he said, "Whose part is the larger, I wonder? I have done more here to diminish the Northern ranks than twenty of Lee's companies could manage."

At that, anger crawled in me, setting me to shaking, and only Illinois' touch on my hand kept me still.

"They'll shoot you if you rush him. Don't give him cause to add another death to his tally now. His time will come," he whispered.

So I kept still, despite the anger coursing through me. But I must confess, seeing the confidence in Winder's stride, the well fed jowls such a contrast to my companion's sunken face, that I found myself doubting for the first time. This was hell. Would our side come for us, so far here in the South?

Winder kept our rations from us that night, although no man had broken rank.

***

The Raiders grew bolder and bolder. Every day, they preyed on the weak. Some poor souls had cracked, and they wandered like shaggy ghosts through the camp, stumbling, sometimes babbling or singing to themselves. The Raiders amused themselves by edging the men towards the "dead line" that circled us, marked with a flimsy bit of wood, some ten feet away from the stockade wall. Step over that and the guards would shoot you. The Raiders would come up and ring some fellow, shove him from one to another, laughing uproariously, and when the game was over, they'd push him towards the line and laugh even harder when a shot rang out and he fell.

"Can't anyone do anything?" I said to Illinois. "Winder won't."

Illinois looked me over before nodding at another man sitting near us. "Sergeant Leroy has been talking to me about that. Go fetch me Limber Jim and Ned Carrigan. And keep your mouth shut. If they find out we're planning something, we're sunk."

That was the day the plan was born.

***

Sergeant Leroy Key was a tall man, but sparse-fleshed. He was a Westerner, also from the state of Illinois, and with my exception, kept his plan confined to other Westerners. He told the guards of his plan and somehow got it approved.

Why did the guards agree? To them it was an amusement to see us trying to regulate ourselves. I do not think that most of them considered us human. To see one of them leaning from his tower, eyeing a man staggering too close to the deadline, raising his rifle to shoot and then boasting to his fellows that he killed a Yank was not uncommon.

Key kept it as secret as he could but we knew the Raiders had learned of it when they tried to drag him out of what he called his tent, but was really a blanket-covered hole dug into sandy slope, in order to kill him. He fought them off; told the rest of us that we'd move the next day.

That was when I finally encountered Jimmy Sunshine again. We were both up at the creek mouth, filling buckets. He gave me an unfriendly look from his eyes, still blue but no longer so innocent.

"You an yer friends think you can come up against us?"

"I know you," I said.

"Sure you do. I was there that first night you came in, I remember."

I shook my head. "No," I said. "We met in New York."

For the first time a look of interest came into his face. It transformed it, made it something human other than the devilish sneer that rode it. "Yeah? When?"

"You tried to pick my pocket."

His face closed to me.

But I hadn't meant it as an accusation. I wanted to ask him how he had come to this pass, how the war had treated him, how he had come to Andersonville.

But he turned away with his bucket. As he went, he tossed over his shoulder, "You'll see. Ya think ya are all so high and mighty but we run this place."

"For now," I said, but so softly he could not hear me.

***

You would have thought the Raiders learning of our plans a setback, but it proved the opposite. For word got to others. All of those who had suffered under their depredations now thought that perhaps our movement might succeed. They gave off discussing escape or how best to cook the daily meal ration (dumplings, gruel, or cakes) and all the talk was about us, and whether or not we would succeed.

That night, the Raiders sang in their tent, howling out the words in triumph. They thought there was no way we might prevail, and they celebrated their victory in advance, buying sorghum whiskey from the guards.

And so in the morning, we marched on them.

We had armed ourselves with clubs. All the camp had gathered to watch us, 15,000 men or so, standing on the hillside, a solid mass of faces.

We marched on them as orderly as any soldiers' company. And then the fight began and all became chaos.

I have had enough of war; I will not speak of my actions on that day.

***

When all of it was over, we had captured the Raiders and confined them to the small stockade the guards had agreed to let us use.

Key made sure that all of the formalities were observed. He organized a court-martial, finding thirteen sergeants, and making sure that all of them were as new to the prison as could be, in order that they would hold no prejudices. The accused were confronted by witnesses, they were allowed a defense, and in the end six of them were sent to hang.

Jimmy Sunshine was not among the six. He was not important, not a leader. He was among the hundred or so that were left.

"What will happen now?" I asked Illinois.

He said, "We'll have to let them out of the stockade."

I was outraged and said so. "So they'll all just get off scott free?"

"Oh no," said Illinois. His voice was sad and tired. "They won't." He pointed near the stockade and I saw the crowd gathering at the gate.

They formed two parallel lines, lines made of hundreds of men, most still carrying those clubs.

The sight filled me with satisfaction. I pushed my way into one of the lines. We waited.

When the first raider stepped through the gate, his face pale with apprehension, a great sigh of satisfaction went up from the crowd. He took to his heels immediately, realizing the situation, but the crowd would not let him break out of the lines. Instead he ran between them and the blows fell on him as he ran.

When I saw Jimmy Sunshine prodded through the gate, I raised my club and waited.

He ran quickly, his arms raised to protect his face, wavering from side to side as blows landed. Just as he came to me, he staggered in the sand, going to his knees, his sweat-sodden black hair clinging to his scalp, bruises already blooming all along his forearms and face.

Until that moment I had been filled with rage. So many moments fueled it: my comrades dying of gangrene or dysentery, the careless laughs of the guards after shooting a man, the black mane of my horse fluttering as he cantered away from me with a Rebel soldier on his back. That soldier had not meant to hurt me so, he had only been doing what he was meant to do, but the Raiders had betrayed their own. Had committed evil intentionally, and this boy was among them. My jaw clenched; my fingers tightened.

He lifted his blue eyes, wide and desperate, to mine, and saw my anger. He tried to pull away, even as my hand lifted.

I thought of all that had been taken from me.

If I struck him, though, I would lose even more.

I dropped the club on the sand and he staggered back to his feet and kept running. He ran like a black horse, and at least one of us was, for a moment, free.

CHAPTER 17
SENTIMENT OR EMOTION

What it is

You may want to create a story that evokes a specific emotion in a reader. This is a valid goal, and when reviewers accuse a story of being emotionally manipulative, in my experience what they mean is that the strings are a bit too obvious, which no reader likes. It's okay to manipulate a reader—it is the essence of what we do. But an author can never afford to remind a reader that they are reading.

You may be wondering if it's okay to sit down and think, "I'm going to create a story that makes people sad." Sure. Any motivation for writing a story is valid. Just be sure that the story that emerges is something that provides your own unique take on that emotion.

What it provides

On the face of things, this gives you very little: an emotion. But it's possible to extrapolate outward from that if you spend some time thinking about moments of that emotion in your own life, what evokes the emotion both traditionally and personally, and how that emotion plays into daily life.

Considerations

Some story structures are an automatic fit for specific emotions, such as a classic love story. You may choose to work with one of these structures or you may try to subvert or adapt it to your own purposes.

You really do need to spend time thinking about the emotion and manifestations of it in your life as well as the physical details of how that emotion feels when you're in the sway of it: jaw gripped tight or loose and smiling? Eyes narrowed or wide? Shoulders hunched forward or open?

Pitfalls

Your story is cliché. This may be because the emotion that you are attempting to evoke is trite; other times because you are not pushing hard enough to find an interesting emotional core.

The story is predictable. This is because we have plenty of such stories in our canon, and they're something that visual media like movies and television shows often draw on. Here connecting yourself with the emotion may lead in the right direction, but when in trouble also don't forget that it's hard to go wrong by complicating a character's life or raising the stakes.

Next steps

Figuring out the plot of the story is the crucial step without which you're not goign to be able to go much farther. I would suggest you do so by focusing on either characters, conflict, or plot.

Pick one of the the three and think about a manifestation that you would associate with the emotion. For example, character and anger: what sort of people feel extraordinary degrees (either a great deal or none at all) of that emotion? What sort of person do you associate with anger? Are there professions where anger is an asset?

Exercises

1. Brainstorm the emotion. Write a poem, create a collage, draw a picture. Create a list of physical sensations you associate with it. OA: Do a lot of this.
2. Write a 100-250 word interior monologue from the point of view of your main character, thinking about the emotion that you are exploring in the story. OA: Do this for every character that has a speaking part in the story.
3. Write a brief scene that will not appear in the story but shows some of the main character's history with the emotion: either a time they have acted out the emotion or seen it acted out. OA: Do this for every character that has a speaking part in the story.

Case study: (The Owlkit)

I like the occasional sappy story as much as the next person (assuming that they like such things). So I set out to write one by creating a super-cute protagonist, the owlkit, who is partially based on my other cat, a little tortoiseshell named Taco Cat, who also makes an appearance in "Tortoiseshell Cats Are Not Refundable".

To yank on the heartstrings further, I made her pregnant and homeless, and attempting to win a home through her own cleverness. She's someone the reader can admire, resourceful and resilient.

It's a fun little story, and I am pretty sure owlkits will appear in at least a few more stories yet to come. And such a story had to have a happy ending, particularly when it involved Taco!

The Owlkit, the Candymaker, the Beekeeper, and the Brewer

This is a story of Serendib, the city that has a doorway on every dimension except one. The city made of contradictions and juxtapositions, where anything and everything may be sought and found, and it is a city full of the stories that travelers have brought to it, but the city has its own history, which only its natives know. This is one of those secret stories.

Once upon a time there was an owlkit. It was a creature that was partially tortoiseshell cat, and partially gray owl, and just a drop of spidermonkey, and one touch of marsupial, for it had a little pouch where it hid things sometimes. It had great tufted ears and solemn green eyes, and its hunting sound was an interrogatory little prrt? as though questioning the whereabouts of her prey, for this owlkit was also female, and pregnant, and alone when it chanced on Serendib.

She was quick to realize what she had found, and for a week or two she lived on alley scraps and market gleanings, but there are plenty who live off the city's excess, and more than once the owlkit found herself challenged in a way even her sharp little ivory claws could not fend off.

And so she decided to look around for a better arrangement.

The first establishment she chanced on was that of a candymaker, and moreover, a master of his art. Beltray made soldiers of marzipan, complete with war veterans that had tiny honied scars and false limbs made of spun sugar. He made layered candies whose taste slid from intoxicating to illuminating to a moment of such sweetness that your fingers would curl and your eyes close as your tongue chased the last bit of savor. He knew every spice that could be used, and its medicinal and perfumery uses, as well as the seventeen sacred spice combinations of the bakers to the Empress of the Rose Kingdom, and could replicate any confectionary a tourist to Serendib might name.

His establishment faced the street with a green door studded with gumdrops and peppermint wheels (resurfaced every third day by apprentices in the early hours of the morning) and windows showing cases of sugar castles and spun syrup birds, bins of penny candy, and tray after tray of chocolate: scented with cinnamon and cardamon, flavored with ground nuts, flecked with bits of salt or pepper flakes, and plain, from bittersweet to white.

The owlkit slipped in while a customer was entering, concealing itself in the swirl of the man's cloak. The air here smelled of sugar and butter and chocolate, and the owlkit's whiskers quivered with curiosity and delight. It slipped along the side of the shop, trying to stay out of sight but a woman shrieked and suddenly everyone was looking at it.

The owlkit did what an owlkit does best, which was to look adorable. Its tufted ears trembled as though slightly timorous, and it opened its great green eyes to the maximum.

"Ohhhhhhh, precious!" The owlkit found herself swept up in arms that smelled of sweetness, cradled to a white apron. It was Beltray himself, who had a heart as soft as a marshmallow and a great fondness for small animals. And while a few apprentices eyed the owlkit sidelong, no one said anything to contradict Beltray, for he was an artist, and one humors artists, or at least that is the custom in Serendib.

Beltray loved the owlkit from the first moment he laid eyes on it. He carried it around with him, cradled in the crook of his arm. He showed it to everyone, including his friend Dib the brewer and Alys the beekeeper.

Alys came often to visit Beltray, for she was in love with him, although he never spoke to her of such things, only of honey and syrups and sweetnesses that had nothing to do with love. She did not care for the owlkit, for she did not like animals, but she pretended to coo at it and stroke behind its ears. The owlkit knew, and it thought about hissing at her, but Beltray seemed like the sort who would not react well to such behavior. So although its ears flattened just a shade, it tolerated the clumsy touch.

At night, it hunted through the candy-makers kitchen, and found fat mice there, unaccustomed to predators, so plump from their diet of sugar and butter that they scampered clumsily, and were easy enough to catch.

One mouse, finding reserves of strength it had not previously exhibited, gave a mighty leap up, only to find itself doomed, for it had leapt into a vat of sugar syrup. It drowned quickly, and in a flavorful way, and then floated there in the middle of the vat. The owlkit tried to reach it, but could not at first, only managing to get syrup all over itself in the process. Finally, it did, and complicated the mess by putting the candied mouse in its pouch for safekeeping.

A light came on as the apprentices entered for the morning, only to stop in dismay. There were sticky tracks everywhere, and jars knocked over in the chase, and everything was in great disarray. They shouted for Beltray, and he came running, then stopped in the doorway, his mouth an O of dismay.

The owlkit thought uneasily that she might have miscalculated. The expressions on the faces were not pleasant, and it was, even to an owlkit's eyes, a chaotic scene. But Beltray smiled and rushed forward.

"The clever little fluffbird has been catching mice!" he exclaimed, pointing to the sugary tracks and several corpses that the owlkit had been saving for later. "Oh, the darling is trying to work for a living!" He swooped forward and picked her up, and she began to purr. But he exclaimed and held her out. "She's all sticky!" he cried. "We must give her a bath!"

A few moments later, the owlkit had fled the shop, leaving behind several well-scratched and pecked apprentices and the wailing Beltray, still calling after her. She found a spot in the sun and cleaned herself meticulously, down to the last feather, then sat enjoying the warmth and pondering what to do next, her eyes half closed in thought.

When something buzzed past her, she snapped at it and caught it, and chewed thoughtfully. It was a bee, and owlkits love to eat bees. A few more buzzed past, and she ate them, and then a thought came to her, and she followed the next one.

It led her, as one might expect, to the garden housing Alys' hives. And then she made a hearty meal of bees, then laid down in a patch of greenery to sleep and digest. It was there that Alys found her drowsing.

Her first reaction was to drive it away, but she recognized it as the pet that Beltray had showed her, and so she held out her hand and made noises until the owlkit woke and blinked at her. Alys clearly wanted the owlkit to stay there, so of course it followed her into the house, despite the hands she flapped, trying to drive it off. It explored the house while she sent a messenger to Beltray, telling him that his pet was there.

He showed up soon, but the owlkit had not forgotten the mention of a bath. She would not come when he coaxed, and just to demonstrate the utterness of her indignation, she twined around Alys' ankles as though affectionately, which had the bonus delight of irritating the beekeeper in a way she could not react to. (Owlkits are known for the touch of catlike malice in their natures.)

"I'm afraid she has chosen to stay with you," Beltray said gloomily.

"Oh, surely not!" Alys exclaimed with a touch of panic, and tried her best to persuade the candymaker that he should take back the owlkit. But when he said he would certainly come visit it from time to time, she faltered a little. Meanwhile the owlkit acted ever more affectionate towards her, knowing she was forced to reciprocate.

"How you will enjoy the kittens!" Beltray said, and Alys frowned. The owlkit plopped down in a basket and continued to digest bees, acting as though this was her home now. Nonetheless, the owlkit knew that while the situation was momentarily enjoyable (and full of delicious bees), it was hardly suitable for long term. And so she slipped out the door after Alys had gone to bed.

This time, the owlkit knew that she must set her mind to things. The kittens would come soon, and kittens, particularly owlkit kittens, require a safe place where they can flutter and play.

When she came to the brewery, she paused. There were no mice here, for the brewer had invested in clever little mechanicals that scurried about cleaning up the grain. But there were rafters where kittens might play, and a great courtyard that seemed mostly unused. This would do nicely.

She recognized Dib when he came out of the house, and she scampered over and wound around his ankles, purring and being as charming as she could possibly be. But while Dib did not hate animals, he was not particularly interested in them either, and so he simply nudged her away with the toe of his boot. "Shoo!" he said absently, then forgot her and went about his business.

The owlkit pondered this. This was the best place she had found yet to raise her kittens, but unless Dib acknowledged her, it was a flimsy shelter, that she might be driven from. No, she had to make him want her as a pet.

And so the owlkit set herself to charming the brewer. She played, she purred, she posed looking picturesque. The workers liked her, but Dib continued to ignore her, and several times people tried to shoo her out of the brewery entirely. She thought about returning to the candymaker's, but the threat of baths was a powerful one. And Alys didn't like owlkits, and would surely like kittens even less.

She ran after him one day and thought her case finally won, but he paused, looking down at her as she wound frantically around his legs, rubbing her hard little beak on his ankles. "Tomorrow, when you go to the hopgrower, take this along," he told his assistant, pointing down at the owlkit. "We don't have need of it, the mechanicals keep things clean and then some."

The assistant sighed and petted the owlkit, for he liked little animals and had a very soft heart, but feared his master's temper.

The owlkit went away to sit in the sunshine and think. She ate a couple of bees and tried to lie comfortably, but the kits kept kicking and the cobblestones were lumpy against her ribs. She thought back on her experiences, and the meager resources available to her, and eventually came up with a plan.

In the morning that the brewer came in and found something he'd never witnessed before: a mouse floating in one of his beer vats. He shouted for the workers and they came and cleared it away, and just then the owlkit let herself be seen, intently hunting along the corners.

"Well," Dib said, eyeing her. "If she keeps the mice down, then we might as well keep her, I think."

And the owlkit came and wound around his ankles again, and this time he reached down and petted her.

Luckily, the brewer had not examined the mouse too closely at first, and by the time it was fished out, its coating had dissolved. And equally lucky, no one tasted that brew, or they might have wondered at the faint taste of candy that seemed to accompany the hops.

And that is why to this day if you go to the brewery that Dib built and which his descendants run, you will find it full of owlkits, slumbering in the sun and in the shadows, and keeping the establishment free of mice (and bees).

CHAPTER 18
IMITATION, RIFF, OR TRIBUTE

What it is

Sometimes you may love another writer's writing so much that you want to pay tribute to it in some way, to show that you've read it and invite others to do the same. This is something I think of as the Great Conversation between writers, an odd way of calling back to those who wrote before us, and it is one of the things that drives writers.

What it provides

This is a source of both inspirations and constrictions. What this gives you depends on who you are imitating and how slavishly you want to follow their pattern. If it's a writer from a particular time period, you may be constricted to that particular time period and its conventions, for instance.

Considerations

If you want to make sure your writing has the right flavor, make sure you spend some time immersed in the original sauce. Re-read the work you're referencing—a lot of it and preferably aloud. Do it in an empty room, projecting to the corners, feeling the words echo through you.

What is it about the other writer or their work that speaks to you, that makes you want to write about it? How would you describe it? How might you imitate it? How might you refine it and make it better (if possible)?

Pitfalls

You don't want to create what's called a pastiche, an imitation that's just a mashup of what's distinctive about the writing style of the person you are imitating. You must bring something to the table yourself, must be unafraid to leave your own mark on it as well.

Next steps

Identify the plot that you are going to use, first by determining whether you mean to borrow one of the writer's plots or create one of your own. If the former, you will need to figure out which one as well as the chronology and scenes with which you plan to tell it. This strategy includes picking a plot and deliberately skewing, thwarting, or otherwise twisting it to your own purposes.

Read deeply in the writer you are imitating, but also some of their contemporaries. Make sure that you understand the economic and historical context in which they were writing.

Exercises

1. If other writers have written tributes to the writer you are using, read some of their work. What commonalities and dissimilarities do you notice? Are any markedly more (or less) effective than the others? OA: Up the amount of writing and write an essay or blog post about the results.

2. Write down the reasons this writer appeals to you. What are the three pieces by them that you love the most? (If they have only written one work, then select three moments within that work that you particularly love).
3. Read a biography of the author and try writing a letter of advice from them to you on how to best write your story.

Case study: (Bus Ride to Mars)

I love Geoffrey Chaucer and have ever since I first encountered his writing. If he were alive today, I would be writing him fan letters. It's a love affair that began in a college class where Dr. Leslie Martin made us read aloud from the prologue to *The Canterbury Tales*, and continued as I worked my way through all his words.

"Bus Ride to Mars" is my tribute to *The Canterbury Tales*, a work that I love for many reasons, one of which is that it's made up of stories that a bunch of pilgrims tell each other while on pilgrimage to Canterbury. I started with the idea that I would riff on the Tales, and that it would take place on a bus ride to an odd place. I began with Djuna (a name taken from another favorite writer, Djuna Barnes) getting on a bus that was actually a journey to the afterlife. I loved describing what she saw outside the windows as well as on the bus, but all of that was a frame for the stories she overhears, much like the original version. Each of the stories she hears maps to a tale from the original text, and doing those translations was a great deal of fun.

Bus Ride to Mars

Day One

After Djuna had been ushered outside by the men in dark sunglasses, she realized it was cold, even though yesterday had been balmy. Spring's uncertain chill chased her up the steps into the bus's welcome heat. Even cold, though, it was spring, and she wavered on the very last step, suitcase in front of her like a wall, thinking, "My fiftieth spring on Earth, can I really leave that?" Then someone pushed at her from behind and she went in.

Wider than most, the bus took up one of the highway's double lanes. Inside two aisles ran between three banks of seats upholstered in royal blue, squares of clear plastic clamped onto each headrest. Shadows pocked the aluminum floor.

The bus shuddered away from the curb. Azaleas bloomed in each yard, mop-heads of purple and pink and crimson and the occasional yellow.

They left the neighborhood behind and passed through a wooded area on the town's edge. Fenced-off trees bore carvings featuring pluses and hearts and arrows and one mysterious biohazard marking. Was it warning her, confirming every misgiving about this journey? She could have stayed, somehow. Would have stayed, somehow, refused to remove herself from her house despite the polite gentle insistence of the spirits in black. Could she touch the cord, bring the bus to a stop, get off, walk back home? She flexed her hand, looking up, but made no move to rise.

When in doubt, eat. She'd packed a hamper. Two sandwiches, bacon and crunchy peanut butter, four more peanut butter on whole wheat, a cooler with four strawberry yogurts and a gamepiece's worth of cheesecake among the ice packs, baby carrots and a stalk of celery in a baggie. A dozen juice boxes. Tofu cubes marinated in sesame oil and soy sauce, and squishy avocado wrapped up in nori. That was lunch for today, in a few hours.

She had two carrots now, biting them off with angry snaps. She'd set off and now here she went, despite the fact that she'd rather stay home, to Mars, which was also the Afterlife, somehow.

The air smelled like old French fries and stale donuts. An unceasing fan blew down on Djuna, making her extract a sweater from her carry-on. She had never expected the Afterlife to have a temperature.

At the front the robot driver, tireless, drove without ceasing on its own behalf, although she'd been told it would park every six to twelve hours for the benefit of its passengers. It wore an absurd blue plastic hat and no other illusion of clothes.

The windows with which the outermost seats were privileged featured mask-sized ovals with plastic shutters. Two-thirds of the way back in the bus, Djuna slid the shutter closed, leaving a slit of brilliance.

From her vantage point, she could see most of the bus and her fellow travelers. She'd treated it like any other journey. She'd hoisted her rollaway in the overhead shelf, dumped her shoulder bag and coat on the middle seat to discourage seat seekers, and shoved her paperback in the middle seat pocket. The book's cover showed a dolphin curved around a woman, titled FORBIDDEN WATERS: A REAL LIFE ODYSSEY INTO INTER-RACIAL PASSION, blue and silver foil waves shimmering around the couple.

She hooked the Traveler's Marvelous Window Garden's suction cups below the window's lip. A silly souvenir bought at the station. She did not read the 8 point font descriptions on the seed packets, simply shook vermiculite particles like mica grit from their puffs of plastic, into the windowbox. She planted and watered, and read the first two pages of her book and ate another carrot. She was in it for the long haul, the five day trip to Paradise, Mars.

Most of the other travelers were nondescript. A few stood out, particularly a young woman all in pink and gold, dark hair, a spiral unicorn horn – Djuna couldn't guess whether it was cosmeticked there or some mark of Faerie. Her eyes were saltwater deep, blue as storms. She sat near the front, just behind the driver.

An elderly man in a slouchy cap stared at her briefly, like an arborist examining a tree, assessing her height and blossom schedule and composition, before going to the back of the bus and sitting down with a sulfur-scented huff.

A trio of identical blonde... girls? Young women? Hovering on the edge of adulthood, maybe a little past. They were late getting on. They wavered near her row, clearly thinking three of us, one of you, but she buried her nose in her book and refused to look up. One cleared her throat, but the others tugged her over to a middle row, towards the back.

Triumphant, Djuna ate another carrot, more slowly this time. She looked out the window. Thunder Lanes Bowling. Lightning Shoes. Kang Acupuncture and Herbal Medicine. Fungi Fun-Go. Mi-go Me-go. Shoggoths-R-Us. Strip malls and lanes of traffic. Spirit houses beside the road, edged with gold and crimson paint. She thought of her little house, of the intricate banisters, the upstairs and downstairs she had furnished with her thoughts, her dreams, her china cupboards.

The red-haired kid a few seats up tried to explain his hand-held game to his mother again while she carried on a conversation on her cell. "You can be animal, vegetable or mineral," he said.

"Yeah, yeah."

"I control my race's starting philosophy."

"Yeah, yeah."

"I'm warlike and spiritual."

She took her attention from the phone. "How can you be warlike and spiritual? Isn't that a contradiction?"

"Aztecs were warlike and spiritual. I was reading a book about them the other day. They had these sacred warriors, Jaguar warriors."

She snorted but said into the phone, "Will the house be ready? By ready, I mean completely ready. I want linens on the beds and groceries in the cupboards." Then with a shift of tone. "Yes, we'll be fine, the seats are big and he can sleep in them. Yes, I have all of his medication. Bye." She flipped the phone closed and stared at the concavities on the floor, pressing her hands together as though praying.

"Mom? Mom!"

"Jaguar warriors," she said in a weary tone. "Listen, do you want to hear a story about Jaguar warriors?"

"Yeah," he said warily, as though unsure what he was agreeing to.

"Once upon a time, there was a king named Gil."

"Was he a Jaguar warrior?"

"He was a warrior king, fierce as a Jaguar. He ruled his kingdom with a fair and gentle hand, but every time he went out to speak to his people, the people he'd agreed to govern, to oversee, to be the head to, he'd get this sad look on his face. They'd ask him what was wrong, and he'd look away at the horizon with a sad and noble face and shake his head. This was infuriating."

"Infuriating?"

Djuna ate her nori lump by squishy avocado lump, chasing the melt around the roof of her mouth with a tongue tip as shr listened. The Traveler's Garden sent out a hesitant smell of rain.

"Infuriating. Because, after all, what were his people supposed to say to that? He was clearly unhappy but he refused to say anything. And then, eventually, he put aside his crown and went walking down the road, and blamed it all on the unhappiness he never would explain to them."

There was a silence before the kid spoke again, voice like an uncertain snail's horns emerging. "Is this story really about Jaguar warriors?"

"It started out that way," she said. "Then it all went pear-shaped, and I don't know when."

Silence stretched between them. A few seats forward, a nerdy boy was interviewing the unicorn girl. She spoke in upper-class, almost accentless English.

"My name is Cristen Night," she said, blinking at the camera. "What should I say?"

"Talk about anything. Talk about what sort of TV you like to watch."

"I like to watch that new show, These. You know the one? It's been around for two seasons, just starting the third."

Nerdboy made a noncommittal sound, gestured at her to keep talking.

"There's the main character, King T, who's married the Queen of the Centaurs and brought her and her sister Emily to live in his palace. It's like a huge cloud castle, all misty white corridors and you know, atmosphere."

The plastic creaked as she shifted against it, getting more animated. "The actor they have playing him is all-vid, latest gen algorithm. Kurt Destiny is the brand. So swank! Dublicious. Anyhow, he was getting married at the end of last season, and all these glims in black show up, laced and gothy. They're wailing and beating on these hand-held drums they wear around their necks. He asks who they are, and they turn out to be genetic constructs whose male counterparts, like their twins, have all died out due to a bad DNA twist. All bereft, widowed twins. They tell him they need him to wrestle this minotaur thing."

"Why?" Nerdboy adjusted his camera, brought the focus even closer in on her face, her perfect eyes, polished horn gleaming like mother of pearl in the bus's overhead lighting.

She shrugged. "Television." She continued on.

"There's these two PoWs, Palamon and Arcite. They are in this tower and look out, and see Em – that's the Queen's skanky sister – in the garden, her arms full of red and white roses, and more growing from her jacket. They're big bang crush right off on her, and they start fighting over who loves her the most. Then Arcite gets freed and they argue over who's better off, Palamon, who has the chance of glimpsing her every day, or Arcite, who can go home and raise an army to come and get her with."

The bus jerked to a stop. This close to the sea, salt water rode the wind.

After dinner, the smokers excused themselves as soon as possible from the meal to go outside and power through cigarettes or thin cigars as fast as possible. The man in the suit didn't even pretend to eat, just ordered a large coffee, black. He took it outside. By the time Djuna came out of the burger taco squid joint, cigarette butts mounded by the heel of his black snakeskin shoe.

Later some riders watched the evening news on the bus TV screen, which hung down to the driver's right. The light was blue and soothing. With headphones in, all she saw was the flicker of faces. Later, she took the headphones out and leaned back. Someone behind her was telling this story:

"I knew this kid, he was a game developer, got snagged by a company fast out of college, bright kid, worked hard, played hard, did a lot of mountain climbing, kayaking, that sort of thing. Truth be told, he was stronger, had a bit more swagger, than the average geek at his company and he became a bully, lorded it over the other devs, and the company let him get away with it because he had the programming chops to back it up.

"He married the CEO's daughter, a bright young Wellesley grad, a geek's daughter, who loved online games as much as any solitary nerdy kid that had been raised on World of Warcraft.

"He was one of those weird, obsessive kids and he noticed his wife spending a lot of time playing online games. He'd go and make characters on whatever server his wife was playing on and go grief kill anyone she was flirting with. Over and over again.

"He kept on doing this, rather than working on the games he'd been hired for. He'd try to get his wife into the betas of the games, but she was onto him by that point, I think, wouldn't log into any virtual world he was in, said he was too intense, and of course that just made him more intense.

"When his manager talked to him about his job, he went nutso and accused the manager of having virtually seduced the wife. He'd noticed her playing this one online game, Paradise Garden, an adult encounter game, and when he'd tried to join it, he learned his IP was banned, and all of his credit cards. He said the manager ran the game and that was how the game knew to ban him.

"He went to some sort of halfway house for people that the Internet had damaged. And while he was there, he took up in an online relationship with some kid on Mars."

"And you know him, or you know this kid?"

"I'm him. I'm going to meet the kid."

Silence. Djuna wondered what he looked like. The other voice said, "I thought you said he was young."

"Sure. Twenty years ago, before he went into jail and then the house. He was young back then. I was young back then."

"How old is the kid you're going to meet?"

"She's 18. Cute and smart and funny, and wants someone to help her run the restaurant she inherited. Life's good." He drummed restlessly on the back of the seat, and she wondered again who he was, which of the crowd he was, as he repeated himself. "Life's good."

Day Two

In the rumble of early morning, the Traveler's Marvelous Window Garden was filled with silvery green shoots, soft as toothbrush bristles. Djuna ran her palm over the surface and stared outside. A construction site surrounded the highway, orange plastic, then yellow, then olive green, then concentration blue, and tangles of machines and signs that pointed forward and backward, up and down. The bus lurched, swaying from lane to lane.

Like everyone else, she conducted her morning wash in the bathroom, and was glad the bus wasn't more crowded. She stared at her too-pale face in the jerk-surfaced mirror as she brushed the flavor of last night from her mouth and washed her hands with vanilla ginseng bubble pearl soap. She didn't bruise herself changing into a fresh shirt from her bag, even though she collided with the walls. She'd always bruised easily, banged into door frames and tripped on missing top stairs. She'd lost the ability to be bruised, though, somewhere along the way.

Was that how it went, were the dead unaffected by any events? Was that why they resorted to story after story, half-glimpsed or fragmentary or laboriously whole? They were all the same effort.

When she returned to her seat, she found that the bus had entered the Underwater Tunnel. Outside, she could see the rivets and glass holding back seawater, and the silvery slide of fish every once in a while. The children were glued to the window, and the three blondes stood near the forward luggage rack, taking turns to gaze out. One of them flicked her hair back, away from their flat smooth forehead, and within a few seconds, the others followed suit, made the same gesture.

Behind her – which was the Internet junkie, on his trip to meet a kid, a child? Was it the flat-faced, pleasant-haired man, or the one beside him, who looked surlier, bruised like a peach bounced down the road by life. Maybe that tubby middle-aged man wearing the Darth Vaderix Giz-Pop t-shirt or the very polite looking elderly man. Two looked back at her then let their eyes slide away.

Later that day, around two o'clock bus time, or so the buzz went, they'd be stopping in Elfland as they passed through. Just as one of the blonde girls, who said her name was Magda, confided this to Djuna, the robot driver announced it over the intercom.

Its voice buzzed like a wasp: At 2:35 PM, we will be stopping at the Elfland Border Park and Shop. You will have one hour, fifteen minutes for meal and recreational purposes. Please return to the bus promptly at the appointed time. The announcement stopped with an admonitory pop and crackle of static and the robot continued staring forward, its metal claws buried in the steering column, maneuvering the bus along the twenty-lane highway.

Signs swooshed past, underwater settlements, sometimes just single homes clinging to the side of the tunnel like a barnacled bubble: Who-ville, Perelandra, Surf N' Turf, Dagon's Deeps, Bucket and Tub, Tile Place, Atlantis. Atlantis looked like a fancy resort. Buses and small, gimcrack cars with their tops down filled its parking lot to its attendant booth gills. Djuna counted cars and tried to convince herself that she wasn't really on the way to Mars. She was at home, snug in bed or on the couch with a cat curled on her stomach.

Who would be feeding her cats?

The red-haired boy told his mother that his civilization just completed the pyramids.

"Did you build the Sphinx too?" she asked, but he didn't know what that was. The mother returned to her phone conversation. They were arguing about interiors and paint and why she didn't just fly there. She said, voice pinched tight with anger, "You're always complaining about the cost of things. I thought you'd appreciate the gesture." The phone clicked as she turned it off.

Nerdboy was interviewing a bristle-haired woman, standing with his camera transfixed by her face.

"My name is Tulip Song," she said. Her face was lined as though by weather, but a chemical edge to the redness made Djuna think she was younger than originally estimated.

"Are you going to Paradise?" Nerdboy asked. He smirked, and Djuna sensed a tagline for the documentary in his head. Are you going to Paradise? Indeed.

She said, "I am."

"In order to..."

"I'm going to visit my childhood servant."

Did she say servant or sweetheart? Djuna wasn't sure, and her following words didn't point her in either direction.

"A little girl name of Laura – I haven't seen her in over half a century! Oh, how I look forward to seeing her!"

In Djuna's book, the woman wondered if the dolphin really liked her while the dolphin wondered if she really liked him.

Tulip Song simpered but said nothing more about Laura. Djuna wondered what Laura thought, waiting for the child mistress. What would it be like to grow up with servants at hand? Who did that, any more?

Elfland was disappointing, too neon and clove scented, too ready to hawk jeweled bridles and flasks of love potions. The passengers ate a late lunch there, including fresh fruit from the little goblins hawking grapes and strawberries and apricots in the rest stop parking lot. Djuna sat among the ancient oaks, filled with gloom and doom and signs warning her not to go too far into the trees.

The cheap fruit was sweet, so delicious that she ate it all within an hour or two of having re-boarded the bus, which swayed its way up the Elfland Entrance Ramp, 77BAA. She licked her fingers clean long past the time when the savor had left them. This would have embarrassed her more if she hadn't noticed others doing the same. The children were uniformly asleep, drooling like opium smokers. The elderly man had bought a birdcage with three blue butterflies in it. They sang the same tiny shrill song, over and over again.

Mr. Suit had bought more than fruit – he drank from a little golden flask. Restless, he paced around the inside of the bus. Finally he leaned over the back of the seat in front of her and said, "Hey, you?"

She squinted at him.

He squinted back. "You look like a palm reader. You read palms?"

She shook her head.

His eyes squinted harder. Dirt lined his collar and stubble sprang out on his jawline like an untamed assertion.

"I knew a palm reader lived in a guy's house one time, upstairs in the spare bedroom, 500 socks a week including breakfast and Sunday dinners. Real pig too, had piles and piles of books and noodle cartons.

"His landlord was a regular guy, a carpenter. Had just re-married after his wife died from being hit by a garbage truck. Sweet little thing, just barely legal, his dead wife's sister." He exhaled and she could smell the fairy brandy on his breath. "Puppet pretty.

"The carpenter's out one weekend, helping the guy next door build a miniature golf course. They've been working on it for a while, it's going to help fund their early retirements. She's doing laundry and cooking lunch and the palm reader catches her in the stairway, halfway between the first and second floor. He can see her husband next door, building something that looks like a wooden snowman."

He paused dreamily, closing his eyes and breathing out a second invasion of alcoholic air. Behind her, the caged butterflies began their song again.

"He takes her hands and leans in close, telling her he'll read her fate in her palms, turns them over like soft little doves to examine their bellies, releases one in order to trace the other with a fingertip, running his nail up from the wrist towards the fingers, along the life line, then strokes it from left to right, wavering between the love and fame lines."

Every word made her more uncomfortable. There was something

about his face, as though he'd forgotten she was there, as though he was telling himself the story and had forgotten the punch line.

"He brings her wrists to his lips, still looking out at her husband and the pine skeleton of the snowman and browses along the skin there. But she manages to yank away, looking out the window herself. She pulls up the window, sticks her head out, shouts and waves to her husband while the palm reader shrinks back against the wall. She doesn't say anything like hey, the boarder is hitting on me, though. Just says hi to her husband, and then pulls her head back in, shuts the window, and says to him, My husband's the jealous type. Anything you're proposing to me, you better be factoring that in."

Man in a Suit breathed out, breathed in, and out again. Djuna wondered whether he was falling asleep, but he opened his bloodshot eyes and said, "And he did. He factored that in quite adequately."

His voice was bleak as air-conditioning. He said the last part again, as though worried she might miss its meaning, "Quite adequately."

Djuna didn't answer and he went on. "The carpenter was going out of town to a meeting of his church. Had I mentioned he was a religious man, a deacon of the Fist of the Luminescent Salvation, a first-class deacon, no less?

"All that she wanted was to sleep in her lover's arms, and that was all he wanted too, he said, envisioning a night of this and that and the other thing. And the next day, the carpenter came home and his wife told him that the palm-reader, Nicholas by name, had been ill and had been staying in his room all this time. A day went by and another, and the carpenter grew uneasy that the palm-reader might have died. He went upstairs and used his master key to open the door and look inside.

"The room was crowded with books and tapestries showing hands and skulls and seas of the moon. Nicholas sat on his bed in lotus position gazing at a tapestry showing a mandala with lotuses blossoming outward.

"The carpenter went to him and shook his shoulder until Nicholas shuddered and came to himself. Gracious, he said, and then thanked the carpenter for waking him from his vision. What was the vision of, the carpenter asked in turn.

Next Monday at a quarter past midnight, it will begin to rain, and rain so hard that it floods all this world, the palm reader said."

The man's suit was the latest cut, but the cheap, shiny material showed threads clumped along one hem. Crumpled Kleenex protruded from his jacket pocket and it looked as though he had been crying. As though he might burst into tears again now unless he was humored.

"And he believed the palm reader?" she said. A dubious twinge tugged at her.

He looked earnest. "Sometimes we aren't raised to question things," he said. "Sometimes we just...sometimes we're as shocked as anyone that things turn out to be different than what they say."

She licked the memory of goblin fruit from her fingers and felt his eyes on her. He was bending forward towards her, almost head to head.

"I need to sleep," she said, uncomfortable at his proximity. She leaned back in her seat and pulled the blanket over her like a shield. She could feel him standing there, staring at her for a few more moments and then he lurched off to the restroom. She heard him retching in there, again and again. She held her fingers up to her nostrils, underneath the blanket, and smelled the apricot perfume on her skin as she licked them again, each finger in careful turn.

Day Three

Today, the plants of the Traveler's Marvelous Window Garden had split into two kinds of plant: a set of heart-shaped, fuzzy leaves and fern fronds salad-suitable, tasting of thyme and lemon when she picked one and ate it.

The bus climbed, up and up, a slant that continued for an hour, maybe more, before they broke into sullen sunlight and saw the Space Needle glimmering, the gulls overhead. The bus stopped for a little while at the station there and the travelers got out to stretch their legs. Three new passengers got on: a pair of tattooed kids, and an elderly woman with short grey hair and no nonsense running shoes. Within a few minutes of her arrival, the man in the slouched hat was next to her, talking. Waiting near the bathroom, Djuna overheard:

"You look at me and you don't see much, but once I was a sales guy, such a sales guy I could sell kittens to cats and the dry litter left over to a cactus. The home office loved me, they sent me to Boston, Bangkok, Berlin, one time to Baltimore, you name it."

"I used to sell things too," she said. "And trade. One time I started with an empty glass jar to trade and ended up with an entire house, and two ponies, and a basket full of mushrooms."

"One time I promised to sell the moon."

"I told a woman I'd give her fifty percent off on true love."

"I got a guy to approach me about buying his mother's name."

"I bought and sold genders, three for a buck."

"Every time I touch a Ouija board, I'm selling ad space in Hell."

There was a congratulation to their tones that made her look hard for horns amid the sparse grey hair, but they looked human enough.

She peed and washed her hands for the fifteenth time this journey, gloomily estimating the cleanliness level by the end of the trip. She made bargains with herself. If anyone complained about the rain, she'd just go home and skip Mars. If anyone said the word "fish" or "petunia". If the red-haired boy completed the Hanging Gardens. If the blonde girls looked at her and smirked one more time. None of this happened.

The man in the suit was gone. Djuna was glad he wasn't continuing to Paradise. Something about the way that he looked at her made her think he would be fine here in Seattle.

Tulip Song was talking to Nerdboy again.

She said to the round-eyed camera: "I once knew this guy, a little rooster of a guy, named Perkins. A party animal, he'd run through your money faster than goose-snot."

"Yeah?" Was that a note of challenge in Nerdboy's reply? Tulip Song kept on like she didn't hear it. She started some long story full of cuff-links and bell jars and errors of circumstance.

But Djuna's attention was caught elsewhere: out on the street an old woman swept with a broom while another one, almost identical, with her skirts hiked up, pissed in the gutter. As she watched, the first woman saw the second, came running, belabored her with the broom while the second continued pissing before gathering herself and scrambling away, smile serene, and heading down the hill where the glitter of sound water awaited.

The stop lasted an hour and a half by the station clock. Then they were on the road again, rolling out over a lake, another lake. Mountains and more lakes and pines. As she watched, the landscape shifted. There were black and white magpies on the fence poles by the time true darkness overtook the bus as it rolled on.

Day Four

The Traveler's Marvelous Window Garden gave Djuna tiny, perfect pears, sweet as melancholy, and stalks of pink-ribbed celery. Around the edges of the box, strawberries were ripening, but still not quite there. She ate a bite of pear, of peanut butter sandwich, of pear, peanut butter, pear as the road rolled past. It was flat here, all monotonous wheat fields and the great green circles of irrigation. The red haired boy's civilization was battling the upstart Persians.

A small town passed by in a succession of churches and garage sales and one monumental ball of twine. The road stretched like string, taut as heartache and goodbye, leading her into the future.

At evening, they pulled into Lawrence and the Burroughs Space Lift. People got out and milled around while waiting for the bus to be loaded into a transport. The station was vast, high-ceilinged. Some of the travelers passing through here were not human: mutants and tentacled Martians, gelatinous Ood and frond-waving Barbai like cinnamon-scented bushes. There were clones and steam-powered constructs and every kind of robot, from a retro, man-muscled brass and silver Adonis to tech robots as boxy and unadorned as vacuum cleaners.

The elderly woman and the man in the slouched hat sat outside in the humid air. Locusts sang in the surrounding cottonwood trees, still spindly new as though less than a decade had passed since their planting.

The air smelled of exhaust and wheat and dying flies. Djuna sat near them and ordered a Tecate and listened. The sugar packets on the table showed a series of zeppelins, balloon bellied and intricate as flowers.

This time the woman was the one doing the talking. She said:

"Once I knew a woman who was a marvelous inventor, who built things of jackstraw and metal gears as thin as paper. She built herself a house that she lived in, like a hermit crab inside its shell, and she kept building inwards, until she grew as thin as a serpent, coiled among her books and magazines and old lanterns."

"What did you sell her?" The man sounded sullen as a chess board, slouched in his seat as though set in cement. "Space?"

She took a drink of milky soda.

"Death," she said. "The ultimate closet." A shiver went down Djuna's spine as they looked at each other.

Later, much later, one of the spirits in black came around, got everyone into the bus before it was loaded onto the transport.

The hamper was almost empty, but Djuna took out the cheesecake as she felt the shudder and grip of the Space Elevator, of the transport moving her up, inexorably, into the sky. She ate it, bite by careful bite, as though saying goodbye to its flavor. She thought about what she'd seen along the way, what she'd heard. Maybe any place was the same as any other. Still, she thought about the red dust of Mars. They said it got into the food, that there was a iron tang to the grit there that you couldn't get anywhere else, that had old Martians licking rust in their retired days in too green places.

She thought about opening the window and crawling out, jumping off into space. What would happen then? It could be anything, really. Like a sit-com or a musical or a wonderful book. She'd always thought it would be pleasant to live in a world where people spontaneously broke into song.

If the window didn't open? She'd have to smash it, perhaps with the heel of her shoe. It would be so complicated and messy, though. Would it really be worth it?

Djuna fell asleep dreaming of the sad surge upwards. Of the struts and wickets of her ascent. Of depressed gremlins clinging to a plane's wing, of balloons at dusk over a prairie's red sweep, of the smell of rain-kissed earth. She dreamed of the life she'd left behind, and told it to herself, but the story was dull, like little pearls of days strung on knotted twine, uniformly even and bland as pudding. When did her story begin? Had it yet? Was it done before it had really begun?

Day Five

The bus was still moving, she could feel it, when she woke in the small hours of the morning. Almost everyone on the bus was. She could hear gentle snores and snorts and the humming of the ventilation system. Outside the stars hurtled past as they went up and up. Below them, the world was the size of a half-shadowed duckpond dwindling to a lilypad.

She contemplated the journey as the bus rose through the darkness. She thought about Point A and Point B and the distance in between. She thought about the impossibility of staying at Point A, of poltergeists and zombies and séances full of dust. When she exhaled, the fronds of her marvelous plant stirred and swayed as though they wanted to whisper something.

She read the last page of her book, and then the advertisements in the back, and then the back cover, and then the numbers of the UPC code. She added them up, and understood what they mean, what the bus represented, and why there was no way to go back. Her story was not done, had not yet experienced its Freitag's triangle, its rising action (though surely she was rising now?), its climax, its denouement like the shuddering release before one curls into the seats knowing that the story is done and the lights will come up soon. Stories flowed around her, predicting and shaping her own, as though now were the moment of her birth, the moment she began to speak.

Red dust dunes pulled past, lazy armadillo shapes repeated over and over again. She looked for fellow characters out in the rusty sand, or even footsteps or a bit of discarded paper, its letters desiccated and spiderlike. But the landscape was an empty frame waiting to be occupied.

The other passengers were restless. The mother spent a solid hour on her phone, ignoring the boy asking her questions, tugging at her sleeve. The unicorn girl could not stare out the window easily; her horn tip collided with the plastic, had knocked it painfully once or twice when the bus had jolted. So she stood near a window, bracing herself with an arm, watching the horizon and the sun glaring censoriously overhead.

They pulled into Paradise at dusk. Djuna left her trash in the seat. Someone would come by and clean it after all, and her finished book would be a bonus prize for some lucky cleaner interested in dolphin sex.

The air smelled of iron as she pulled her rolling bag across the bus's pockmarked floor, exited and inhaled, curious. Glass stretched overhead in an enormous dome, etched with ravens and thunderbirds. Hope entered in at the soles of her feet and made her stand straighter. There was no turning back. This was Paradise, after all.

CHAPTER 19
THEME ANTHOLOGY

What it is

Theme anthologies are perennial creatures: collections organized around a particular concept, ranging from the very loose to the very specific. Some examples:

- *The Machine of Death* anthologies
- Carmen Miranda's *Ghost is Haunting Space Station Three*
- *Shattered Shields*

I do not look for theme anthologies and write for them, because it's my belief that such stories are generally less saleable than those not written to spec. During my tenure at *Fantasy Magazine*, I experienced an onslaught of pirate-themed stories because of a large number of such anthologies and magazine issues in the six months immediately before, to the point where I thoroughly disliked pirates and would begin flinching at the first sound of an Arrr or sign of an eyepatch.

That said, sometimes the idea of a theme story springs into your head, crystallized by the words of the submission call, and it's something that you're excited to write. In which case, go for it. I actually ended up doing two such pirate stories, "Sugar" and "In the Lesser Southern Isles". One sold to the pirate anthology I submitted it to, the other ended up in a different anthology.

But if you're sitting down to write a theme and you're doing it for the sake of something other than the theme or the anthology's cause (Examples: you want to work with a particular editor, you perceive the publication as particularly lucrative or prestigious, etc.) then there is a good chance that what you produce will be lackluster.

What it provides

What such an anthology gives you will differ very much from call to call. It may be just a fragment or a complete plot. Determine what the call in question specifically gives you and then reference that section.

Considerations

If you are sitting down to think up a story for a theme anthology, avoid the first two or three ideas that come to mind. They are low-hanging fruit, easy ideas that will probably occur to more than one writer. Are there interesting ways to approach the material that might be overlooked or under-used? What will readers expect of this kind of story and are there ways you can play upon those expectations?

Sometimes concepts concern a particular piece of science of technology. If so, you do need to understand the science of it, and preferably at better than a surface level. You will also need to extrapolate about it and its possible impact on other things. Think about its everyday use as well as its military implications. Are there industries it might affect, such as communications, energy production, transportation? How might it affect family institutions?

Pitfalls

You're having trouble coming up with ideas. Generally this is a place where I wouldn't push myself too hard unless you have some very compelling reason for wanting to be in this specific anthology. If that's the case, you're probably going to need to do some brainstorming and creativity sparking in whatever form you usually use.

Next steps

Make sure the deadline for the anthology is included in your calendar and you have budgeted enough time for revisions.

Decide what you want to write and make sure you have your basic conflict, characters, and setting. What can you do with the concept or theme that will be interesting and unexpected?

Exercises

1. Because this is such an open-ended way into a story, it's difficult to prescribe exercises that will be useful in all situations. However, let's say all you have is a theme such as a specific holiday: you will want to think about what a reader who has picked up the anthology, based on the theme, expects and wants in their reading.
2. Often editors will find themselves inundated with a particular kind of story. Contact the editor and ask if there is anything in particular that they would like to see. This may help you avoid a situation where someone else has already turned in a story along the same lines as yours, which I have seen happen on more than one occasion. This is another way that procrastinating can harm your publication chances.

Case study: (Hoofsore and Weary)

"Hoofsore and Weary" was written for *Shattered Shields*, a theme anthology with a very broad theme: military fantasy. I decided I wanted to make it a Tabat story, but to use an element that I had been playing around with, the Rose Kingdom, which lies to the southeast. I tried to think of a good military plotline and decided I wanted to do soldiers trying to fight their way back through enemy lines, tempted to give in and not try to get home.

Hoofsore and Weary

They'd shortened the new recruit's name but she wouldn't answer to it. She and the other three musketeers had come on at the last minute. Now here they were trapped in hostile territory, the last of Captain Laws' fighting centaurs, hoofsore and weary, but mustering enough energy to snap at each other somehow.

The Sarge shouldered her way past the others to look at the duo, the new recruit and Jolanda, faced off, fists clenched.

"What's all this?" she said, swatting away yet another stinging fly.

The new recruit was skinny. Insect bites blotched her fair skin around the leather breast harness. She said, scorn in her voice, "I don't have to answer to any name other than my own!"

Jolanda's temper was as quick as her musket. "You're in the Army now, hinny. You'll answer to anything your superiors call you!"

The Sarge stepped forward between the two of them. "Go check the guns, Londa."

"Ain't no use to them with no shot nor powder."

"And if we're lucky enough to find some, I want them ready."

Jolanda grumbled but stepped away.

"Recruit," the Sarge said.

The younger centaur snapped off a salute so precise it could've been made of folded paper. "Sir, yes sir!"

The Sarge said, "At ease." She eyed her youngest soldier. They were down to a couple of fingers over a handful, and had she been able to pick who survived this far, she didn't know that she would've selected this raw newbie, who didn't know how to survive off the land, didn't know the little tricks that kept a soldier moving and, most importantly, didn't know that sometimes you bent for the good of the unit.

"In battle, there's no time for strings of syllables," she said. "Whatever they call you, you answer. Clytemnestra when you're in conversation, but names won't matter when we're fighting. Got that?"

She ran a hand back through her close-cropped hair as the younger centaur nodded reluctantly. The recruit's attitude wasn't endearing her to the older veterans and the usual pranks had been going on. But no time for that now, in the middle of enemy territory. They'd come down through the mountains – and hadn't that been a rabid bitch of a journey? – to hit at the capital, thinking their company would reinforce the siege there. Only to arrive to find it broken, devastation and fire all around.

They'd fought their way out of that, losing most of the company, including the Captain, and struck south, somehow managing to avoid farmers. All but one of them were centaurs, and the territory was hard going, mucky ground that hid deep stones inside it.

What would the Captain have done? Alyssum was scouting and still not back. Sarge fumbled for her pouch, and extracted the map yet again, unfolding it. She'd never been one for books. It was boys' stuff, staying indoors with scrolls and chanting. But the captain had gotten them all to beat their heads against it, even on the field when all they had to read from was their army-issued copy of Rotterdam's Rules And Regulations For Field Cavalry.

They were spending daylight hours on petty squabbles.

"Gear up," she ordered.

Seven, counting herself and the newbie.

Jolanda, shrew-eyed and quick to argue, but the best shot among them. Not that it did them any good without ammunition and powder, all expended fighting their way out of those blood filled streets. Limping now.

Penny, looking cheerful as always, despite the burns weeping along the side of her face, glistening with the last of the field kit's salve.

Alyssum, off scouting, who had drawn black around her face with the ashes of that last fire, till she looked like a tiger with her spiky orange hair. She'd lost her harness, but at least she was small-titted and lean enough to carry it off.

Unlike fat Karas, who was breathing uncomfortable gasps. Her flesh hung loose on her from the mountain journey, and that was back when they'd had rations to carry.

Finally Janna, the only non-centaur among them, lean as a willow, the wicker panniers carrying her snakes sitting low on her hips. At least the snakes were well fed. The Jade Woman's arms were bandaged from their last bivouac, where she'd let her blood into a battered tin cup for the two serpents to lap at. The rest of the company had crowded away, tails and ears flicking, as the snakes, eggshell white and black as jet, crawled over Janna's green skin in a parody of moonlight and shadows before slithering back into their homes.

Now the Jade was sitting in a patch of sun, eyes half closed. She had the knack of the soldier's doze. She opened her eyes as though sensing the sergeant's look and pointed her chin in question.

"Still waiting on Alyssum." The Sarge folded the map and put it away, resisting the urge to look at it one more time. She knew it by heart. A narrow strip of forest edged the settlement ahead, orchards planted to keep back the impassable, bog-ridden marshland. If they could find shelter for tonight, they could slip through that forest and into uninhabited territory, deep woodland where they could make for the coast. It was risky but better than any of the alternatives.

If the captain were here, she'd know what to do. Instead they were playing it all by ear. Sarge had accompanied the captain on three campaigns now. Twice down south to the Windy Plains, where they fought in the sands against serpents and the Jades there. It was where their own Jade had come from, along with the rest of her tribe when they had inexplicably converted to the flag under which Sarge and her captain served.

The Jade had proved herself well enough in the campaign that followed, the season pursuing bandits along the coastline. Still, the Sarge never felt quite sure of the green skinned, redhaired woman who stayed silent whenever possible.

Alyssum slipped back through the underbrush. "There's a hunter's shack up ahead. No one's been in there recent. Spring nearby. No food, but we might scare up some."

"You're sure? How far past it did you scout?"

Alyssum bared her teeth. "Teach your granny to pick ticks... Sir." She drawled out the last scornfully. They had been together in that first campaign where the Sarge had been promoted and Alyssum's resentment at being passed over still lingered.

Sarge looked to see where the others were. Jade had slumped back. The new recruit sulked to one side. Karys and Penny were examining Jolanda's hoof. From here Sarge couldn't tell if it was lost shoe or sprain. Neither was good, when they had a hundred miles to go still.

And no guarantee that the promised boat would be waiting there for them, but they jumped the fence when that came time, assuming they ever got to it.

She took a step forward, shouldered into the smaller woman, using her greater mass to impose.

"I know a cat crawled up your ass about me being in charge, Ally," she said. "But for the love of the triple Goddess, if you don't lay off, it's going to get us all killed."

"If I don't salute right, it's going to see us all dead... Sir?" This time ten times the insolence filled the other's tone.

"Strike off on your own if you want no one in charge but yourself," Penny said, sidling up.

Alyssum wheeled with a convulsive sweep of her hair, ears back.

The air was heated with the smell of sweat. It dripped down the Sarge's neck. A fly landed to sip from the sweat between her shoulder blades and she hitched her shoulders, trying to shake it off. She had a chained set of lumps along one haunch that she suspected harbored parasites already. If they could get someplace where they could build a fire, she could burn them out. Better now than before they grew and swelled, egg-sized lumps. She'd seen plenty of those in her year of duty here in this country. Sweet Lady's tit, she hated this land.

She let none of that show in her eyes as she looked at Alyssum.

The small centaur's gaze tracked between the other two before she dropped her gaze and combed fingers through her hair, wincing at the knots. "Whatever."

"Whatever what?"

Alyssum's head snapped up, eyes narrowed. But she said, "Whatever... Sarge."

***

The Sarge had once asked the captain why she'd been promoted rather than Alyssum or any of the others.

"Why do you think?" the captain had replied. It was an irritating answer, but it was the Captain's way to teach.

"Jolanda's a better shot," she said. "And Alyssum's tough as nails."

"Why does that make them a better choice?"

She struggled for words. She'd never been good at explaining things. "They come from solider families. Grew up training, thinking about it. They're not..."

"Some hoity toity flibbergibbet who ran off to join the Army because she thought it'd be exotic?"

She flushed. She hadn't thought the Captain had caught the words Alyssum had flung the previous day.

"You can tell each's strengths and why they'd make a better Sarge," the Captain said. "You think about the squad overall and where you fit. That's why I picked you."

Those words still warmed her. Of the forty-eight they'd initially had, they were only a handful now. But she'd see those few to the coast.

Or die trying, more probably.

They pushed forward. Dangerous territory. If one human caught sight of them, the alarms would go up and people would be hunting them. If there was a way to avoid that, it should be taken.

The hut wasn't big enough to shelter more than two of them, plus Janna. But there was overhang from its roof, and a fire circle near its front step. They scattered, looking for food. The Sarge rummaged through the hut, but found only a short length of rope and a broken clay jar.

Outside nearby, the recruit was picking berries off of a bush, harvesting them into her helmet.

Sarge said, "You know the drill, soldier."

"But Sarge! These look just like the ones back home!"

"Empty them out. You don't know for sure." Sarge stood over the newbie while the berries tumbled onto the ground. "Now mash them."

"What?"

"Stamp. With your hoof." She illustrated, placing a hoof on the ground and bearing down until it squelched. She lifted her foot to reveal the pulped remains. "That's an order. Squash them."

Step slow and reluctant, Clytemnestra obliged.

"I don't fault the effort," Sarge said. "But stick to what we know we can eat."

They built the smallest of fires. The Sarge had Jolanda take the steel needles from the field kit and heat them in boiling water before she lanced the lumps, extracting each occupant. They had beef tea still, and Alyssum caught a scarf full of frogs, while Penny dug cattail tubers up by the stream.

All in all, it was not the worst meal the sergeant had ever eaten.

She looked around at the faces. They were managing to keep it together even though they knew as well as she did that chances were slim that they'd get out alive. Still they put a brave face on things and pressed forward. That was what one did. What one's duty was.

***

In the middle of the night Karys roused her. She came awake instantly, not sure where she was until Karys said, "I don't like disturbing you, sir, but the new recruit's suffering bad."

The sarge squinted at her, running possibilities through her mind. "Give it to me straight."

"Bellyache and the shits. Bad, both ways."

"Will she be able to travel tomorrow?"

The plump centaur shrugged. "Somewhat. Not as fast as usual. Giving her the last of the ginger from the kit."

"And you woke me because?"

"You're CO. Figure you'd want to know."

Sighing, the Sarge followed her back to where Clytemnestra lay on her side. Centaurs rarely lie down, and the sight of the girl's still face, the hair clinging to her skin in sweat-dampened ringlets, made the sergeant uneasy.

"Ate some berries after all, didn't you?" Sarge stood beside the girl and folded her arms.

The girl moaned something incoherent upward. "Take my braid..." she said. She still wore her hair uncut in the uppercrust fashion, wound around her head, though it was twig-strewn and matted now.

"Not time to think of that now.".

"You don't understand. It's the custom among the high families. You'll give it to the one that loved me."

"I know what you're talking about," the Sarge snapped. "Think you're the first highborn I've ever dealt with?"

If the other newbies had been alive, the Sarge would've made an example of her. Would have toughened her up while teaching the others an object lesson. The captain had been good at that sort of thing. But she was dead and so were the other newbies. No point in anything till they were all out alive.

"We have to stay today, give her a chance to give her to get her legs back underneath her," Karys reported in the morning.

"We don't have time!"

"If she can keep up, we'll be able to move faster. And if your plan depends on moving fast so we don't get spotted, we're going to have to choose between leaving her here or just making up our minds to get caught."

The Sarge chewed her lip, tasting blood where it had cracked.

"Penny says there are more rabbits, and with that rope we can put up snares and catch a few rabbits."

Saliva flooded her mouth at the thought.

"All right. But just one day."

***

The dawn was clear and bright. Sarge had them keep low, and watched the skies for spy birds. Still, they managed to bring water in the canvas bucket and wash each other's hair. The recruit was still ailing, curled up quietly. The others groomed each other and mended tack. Jolanda methodically cleaned all the guns, as though they might chance upon a trove of ammo any moment. There was enough to eat that afternoon, and that night, at least by recent standards.

But at dusk Alyssum, who had been standing lookout, crept in to confer in an urgent whisper. "Think we been made, Sarge. I saw a fellow skulking about in that stand of birches near the spring. He saw me too. He was off quick when he realized I'd spotted him."

Sarge swore under her breath. Alyssum raised an eyebrow. "Ain't heard that one before."

"Jade taught it to me. Go send her to me."

She fingered the paper pouch holding her map. The settlement, once warned, would be waiting for them. The slim hope of the woods had been removed.

Now there was only an impossibility, one the captain herself had warned the sarge away from.

The Jade woman came quickly.

"I need a foretelling," the sergeant said.

Janna nodded. She crouched beside the slumped recruit. The sergeant shook her head. "It's for a choice."

Janna quirked an eyebrow.

"Which way to go," the sergeant said. In the face of the Jade's silence, she added, "It's that or nothing."

"Then you don't need a foretelling. One choice is no choice."

"There are always others," the sergeant said irritably. "We could tie ourselves hands and ankles and hope they'll be kind when they come to take us. I prefer something more active."

Janna's hand hovered on a basket's lid. "What is the question?" she asked.

"If we go the way I'm thinking of, will we die?"

Janna nodded. She reached into the basket, and took out the white snake. It came slowly, winding its head around her arm and then sending it questing out into the air, tongue flickering, flickering. The sarge held herself still to avoid flinching back. Janna came closer, snake winding around her shoulders. As she approached it swayed outward, bringing its face close to that of the sergeant's. Its tongue flickered out, so close to her face that she thought it might lick her nose. She tried not to breathe.

The snake hung in the air, then in a single motion curved back to face its handler. It hovered in front of her face, which had gone slack-jawed and distant-eyed. With unsettling quickness, the snake shot forward, its head striking at the hollow of the Jade's neck, which bore a multitude of small scars. Her eyelids fluttered as the venom struck. Her eyes sank back in their socket, and her cheeks hollowed.

She said, her voice pitched in the low register that she assumed at these times, "Yes, of course some of you will die."

"But who? What path leads to the fewest deaths?" The sarge said.

But it was already too late. Janna's head hung forward in front of herself, heavy as an overladen vine. The sergeant caught her as she fell, and laid her beside the whimpering recruit.

***

She didn't want to tell them what the captain had said about this path, but it seemed unfair not to.

When she repeated the words, the declaration was met with general silence. Then Karys said, "You mean, the captain said that it was the very most dangerous place of all the continent?"

The sergeant nodded.

"Well, ain't that something," Penny said, slapping away a fly. "The sort of thing you get to tell your grandkids." She flicked a look back at Jolanda. The two of them frequently vied over the cuteness of the progeny appearing as a third generation in their families.

"Tough going, I suppose," Jolanda said.

The Sergeant nodded again. "First thornland," she said. "Worse than any you've ever seen."

"Better than sitting here waiting for them to come get us," Karys said.

They packed up the camp, and figured out who would carry Janna and who would help Blackie along.

They sruck east, along a side road, then over fields to what the captain had indeed described as "the very most dangerous place on all the continent". It was where the great barrier surrounding most of this kingdom had originated, through rituals and experiments. It was the heart of the Hedge, and no one knew exactly what lay inside.

***

"I thought the Hedge surrounded most of the border here. Didn't we come in through a split in it?"

"We did." The mountain's rocky foot had given the great vines, as wide around as a centaur's barrel chest, no foothold and so they'd slipped in despite the infamous living wall. "This is unconnected to that heritage. It's the plant they took the magic from."

"Ain't no understanding magic," Penny said.

"Naw," Jolanda said. "You can sometimes and it gets at what she's saying. Magic leaks, it seeps back and forth, and so the original's got a little more magic pumped into it, by virtue of the Hedge holding so much."

"It will be a forest, but bad forest," Sarge said. "Remember that time we went overland to get that bandit camp on that cliff they'd halfway carved into a skull?"

Alyssum's face darkened. That had been terrible going: whippy, saw-edged grass that bit through cloth and leather, midges that clustered on any moist membrane, tufted, hillocky ground that tilted one way, then another, span by span. "That bad?"

"It'll be dangerous," she said.

Alyssum grinned at her. "Don't get much more exotic than this, do it, Sarge?"

They'd enlisted together. Standing in line waiting to talk to a recruiter, she'd confided her reasons for joining up – travel someplace exotic, she'd said, meaning but not saying anything was better than the farm and working in harness their. It had taken too long to find out the other's circumstances – a war orphan, raised by the state, and full of little habits inculcated by years of living in institutions. No wonder Alyssum had mocked her words.

The tone could have been a jibe, but it was friendly, if not particularly respectful. "Aye," she said, and left it at that.

She glanced around. They were ready.

"Let's go."

***

The journey through the mountains had been bad. It featured broken bones and frostbite, short rations and shorter tempers. Half a dozen lost their lives on the trails carved into the mountain's side, usually traversed only in the summer months.

This journey was worse. Thorns and grasses lashed at them, and the stinging insects became great hornets, the size of one's palm, cranky and capable of stinging five or six times in rapid succession, stings like fire that left blood red sores around the stings. The flies bit now, taking nips of flesh.

At first their destination was a green smudge on the horizon, then a wall, stretching up, forty or fifty feet of thorny trees. Brambles snarled the open space between their trunks. Everything was silent except for occasional muted bird noise from outside the trees.

"You have got to be kidding me," Alyssum said.

The Sarge looked at the trees. She hadn't expected them to look quite so grim. But there you go. "We don't have another choice." They followed as she made her way to the clearly delineated edge. You could see bare earth around each tree's foot, except for the wiry black brambles. Outside those margins grass grew. Within them it any other small, weedy plants were unknown.

Everyone's wide-eyed glances showed an edge of panic. The Sarge straightened her back and made her tone matter of fact. "Stay close," she said.

Within moments, the outside world had vanished. The spindly trees towered all around them, even their trunks covered with wicked thorns. The brambles grew at just the right height for tearing at fetlocks and flies swarmed whenever the thorns raked a bloody path across flesh. The Sarge had hoped things would be cooler here along the trees, but somehow it wasn't. They stumbled on. The recruit had recovered enough to walk on her own, although Penny stayed near her, keeping a careful eye out in case she stumbled.

The sunlight filtered through layer after layer of leaves, made the world gray twilight. Now that she was unable to see the sky, the Sarge wasn't sure how much light they had left. They needed shelter, and soon. She called Janna up to her. The woman came with weary eyes. Restless scraping came from inside the baskets as though the snakes knew where they were, and did not approve.

"We need to know the way to go," the Sarge said, almost apologetically.

Jade only nodded. She didn't ask the obvious question: how will you stay on track once I point the way? She knew as well as the Sarge did that this would not be the first time she was asked.

"I don't need to know the route to the coast yet," the Sarge said. "Find something that will help us." She laughed, and the sound of it surprised her. "Bonus if it includes food."

Bitter merriment dried in her throat as the Jade unpacked the snake. It flowed restlessly up and down her arm before sinking its teeth deep into the scar-dimpled flesh. She didn't speak, only pointed.

***

Within a half mile, the ground sloped down abruptly, leading to a thin rivulet, edged with more brambles.

They argued beside the bank whether or not it was safe to drink. Was this the thing that would help them, the Sarge wondered.

With a thrash of water, something exploded from the rivulet, seeming too large to have been contained by the scant water, tearing away the arm Karys had been reaching towards the surface with. She screamed, falling backward.

The Sarge drew the only weapon she had left, the captain's sword, charging forward even as the others scattered. She slashed at the thing's black scales, dripping with dark water, the blade bouncing off ineffectually, the thwarted blow staggering her. It smashed at her, driving her back, and she felt ribs crack under the assault.

The thing reared above her for the deathblow, then paused. She stared up at it in a blaze of pain.

It slumped to the ground, almost crushing her. A spear quivered in its back. Looking across the stream, the Sarge saw a knot of humans in strange spiky armor. She rounded on Janna. "What have we done, that you led us to this treacherous pass, you bitch?" she snapped.

Janna stood her ground. "This is our help," she said, as the others began to wade towards them across the stream.

The Sarge tried to take another breath, but pain and blackness overtook her.

***

When she roused, she was in quiet darkness, inside some structure. One of the humans squatted next to her. She was on the ground, but her ribs had been bandaged and the sharp pains had faded to a soft, woolly awareness of its presence.

Despair managed to insert its fingers around that cloud, pulling it to pieces.

"So we're captured, then," she said, more to herself than to the figure. Capture meant being killed or worse, taken to be interrogated.

The human cocked its head to the side. This close, she could see that the thorny armor was actually its skin, as though thorns grew out from its very bones.

"Captured?" it said, its voice soft, sinuous, and sexless. "No, you have come to succor. This is the village of thorns, where many find refuge."

Hope surged in her. "Refuge?"

"If they choose to give away their memories of what they were once, they can stay here. Most do not come until they are ready for that decision."

She shook her head. "Not that. But will you set us on our way? We are making for the coast."

"In the morning. When all of you have made the decision." He rose to his feet. "Rest now."

***

Lying in the darkness, she ran through the list in her head. She didn't think Karys would have survived. And the others? She ran through them in her head. Who might take such an offer?

Clytemnestra. A chance to escape the life she had chosen, not realizing what choice she had made. Surely the recruit would leap at the chance. And Janna.

And what would the sergeant say to that?

What would the captain have said?

***

In the morning, when they gathered their things, surrounded by the quiet, thorny beings who watched them but said nothing, the Sarge didn't see the recruit. "

Stay and find her?" Alyssum questioned.

"No," the Sarge said, and left it at that. She turned to look at Janna with a raised eyebrow. The green woman shook her head. "We have stories yet together, you and I," she said.

Sarge wasn't sure whether or not that reassured her.

***

But the girl was waiting a little outside the village. The Sarge paused when she saw her. Why had the recruit pressed the issue this way, rather than letting the Sarge simply allow her to slip away? But she fell into line, next to Jolanda.

The Sarge looked at her hard.

"It's my duty," the recruit said, shortly. "I thought about it, Sarge. And I thought, what would you do? And I chose."

What could the sarge say to that? She gestured at them to fall in. Perhaps they'd make it to the coast. Perhaps they wouldn't. But they'd try.

And as she led the way, she stroked the braid of hair around her wrist, the grey-strewn black braid that was the only thing she'd taken, beside the sword, from the Captain's body.

Hoofsore and weary, my love. But I continue on.

CHAPTER 20
COLLABORATION

What it is

A collaboration is the act of writing something with one or more other writers. A collaboration is generally a group effort, and the perception of it is usually that each collaborator contributes an equal amount of work (and genius). Sometimes, more rarely, a collaboration can take the form of one writer giving another a semi-complete piece in order to fix or flesh out.

Collaboration can be a lot of fun when you have the right collaborator. It can also be a terrific learning experience, no matter what the skill level of your collaborator(s), because you can always figure out new stuff from looking at how other people work. When Bud Sparhawk and I collaborated on a novella together, I found Bud's initial process very different from my own, and trying that process out taught me some useful stuff, particularly about the arrangement of stories chronologically (Bud's process was to write everything out consecutively and then go back and rearrange the individual scenes.)

What it provides

A collaboration gives you a wonderful way to come up with things and have your collaborator make them even better.

A collaboration can often help you solve problems with a piece more quickly than you might on your own.

Considerations

Communicate all expectations clearly. Everyone in the collaboration must know what is expected of them, including what the deadlines are. It can be very frustrating to delicately nudge someone only to have them let you know that they've actually been waiting on something from you. I suggest having periodic check-ins when you make sure everything about the process is working for the collaborators, but that approach may seem too touchy-feely to some.

Try to have similar speeds/processes. Matching a very fast writer with a very slow one is a team-up calculated for disaster, unless you make sure that there's some agreement set up ahead of time, and that no one feels they're the major force behind the effort.

Build in a flake-out option. Shit happens. Have a plan for what would happen if one of the collaborators has to drop out - either for the remaining collaborator(s) to fill in for them or an agreement about how a new collaborator might be recruited.

Don't take it too seriously. Collaborations are between friends and peers, and it's important not to let them affect bonds of affection. They're also acts of tremendous trust and to some degree an intimacy that is, perhaps, a dim shadow of what it is to raise a child with someone. Unless you've worked with the collaborator before and know that you can work together, don't absolutely depend on their effort in such a way that you set yourself up to feel screwed over if your collaborator chooses for one reason or another to bail.

Pitfalls

If your collaborator is at a very different skill level than you, the process may prove particularly frustrating.

If your collaborator's process is very different than yours, you may experience difficulties, particularly if your productivity rates differ.

Next steps

One of the greatest joys of the collaborative process, in my opinion, is the initial planning, throwing ideas back and forth and riffing on each other's efforts. Take some time to plan out your piece or if you are both pantsing your way into the project (possible, but in my opinion not entirely advisable) at least plan the process and how you'll be keeping each other aware of your efforts.

Make sure that you and your collaborator are on the same page, so to speak. I know I talked about this in the considerations section, but this is pretty crucial, and it needs to be defined clearly, rather than loosely or vaguely. Set out your calendar, including building in times to check in with each other and see how you're doing. Figure out what the plan is if one of you must drop out suddenly as well as what happens if you disagree about the course of the narrative.

Exercises

1. Write to your collaborator in the persona of one of your characters. OA: Do this multiple times, or else write at length.
2. Try writing different lengths to give each other; swapping after each sentence, then paragraph, then page, then entire scene. OA: try all the lengths.

Case study: (Flying Matilda)

Successful collaborations I have written include *The Surgeon's Tale* (Jeff VanderMeer), *Logic and Magic in the Time of the Boat Lift* (Ben Burgis), and *Flying Matilda* (Gio Clairval). With each of them, the process has been similar—starting with a chunk from one of us, we back and forthed until there was a complete story, then polished.

Flying Matilda

Eery time they saw the apparition, it meant more acrobats would die. Someone would spot him: white trunks, white tunic, floating in the vast billowy confines of the Big Top's canvas ceiling. The nearest acrobat would let out a keening, grief-stricken wail. A body would fall, unfastened from the balloon that had kept it airborne. Then another would plummet, and other, until all lay broken on the ground, balloons spinning free.

The billboards read: "Pale Glow, the Merciless Killer," and: "The Man of Mist Won't Stop Before All Acrobats Are Dead," and: "Pale Glow Hates the Circus!"

The Queen called on the remaining flying acrobats to organize a hunt and bring him down. But at first sight of their foe, most hunters lost their willingness to live. They crashed in the working and living areas; corpses filling stalls, galleries, and stage boxes; carbonized inside braziers; drowned in washing tubs; fractured by fly bars. The staff, from the sound engineers to the paint crews, screamed for ack-ack guns. Most artists embraced cults of vengeful angels. A minority went on strike, climbing the balconies and strewing the galleries with pamphlets and leaflets.

Sensationalist billboards warned: "The Pale Glow Menace: The Public Is Next." Spectators clamored for refunds of admission taxes. The economy of Big Top wavered on the brink of collapse.

A woman, a flying acrobat in her own right (a rarity, a freak), volunteered to lead the hunt. The balloon trick was the most dangerous stunt. No other woman had ever pulled it off; no other woman had ever been allowed to suspend herself by her hair beneath a red and white balloon showing the Queen's face on a yellow background, a face that frowned thoughtfully down at the crowd. Waves of excitement stirred the audience.

"Let the Hunt Begin," blinked the billboards. The public cheered.

Matilda stretched her arms out gracefully, kicked her high-heeled red boots to show she was flying. Framed by aerialists, she rose, and as she rose, her eyes found the haze of the man in white, floating near the spot where the tent pole met cloth. He was translucent; she could see the canvas' rough weave through him.

She bared her teeth. Let him try to claim her. She'd had the best training. Let him try! She rose higher, stern and determined as a flying weasel, white teeth sparkling in a fierce smile.

Down in the circus ring, the last flying acrobats--wearing armors covered with brown sheep's skins, and masks with horns--screamed in defiance. The audience clapped castanets to root them on. Click-clackity-clack.

A hunter strapped to an orange balloon shot upward, followed by a second, and a third. Soon the canvas dome teemed with bright spheres converging on the solitary shape. Matilda glimpsed the translucent figure spread-eagled as bullets hit, drawing sparks from the impenetrable tent surface and the equally impervious balloons. The bittersweet oily odor of burnt gunpowder filled the air.

Pale Glow seemed unaffected.

Hunters tore off masks and horns, despair painted on their faces. The castanets paused each time a body fell, spectators scrambling out of the way.

Matilda glanced at the Queen, who sat in the royal box. Despite the distance, she made out the Queen's smile. Even without looking, she would have known the Queen's posture, her gestures.

She severed the harness imprisoning her hair and freed herself from the balloon. Haloed with soft light, she sped toward her enemy. A million mouths cried in bewilderment. A million castanets stopped rattling, then ripped faster rolls.

Only the Queen's smile showed no surprise.

Shimmer, Pale Glow mouthed. This is not your war. (Her mind swarmed with his words.)

Matilda answered the same silent way: What did you call me?

That's your real name, said the voice in Matilda's head. I thought myself alone. Can't you see we are of the same kind?

Matilda, curious, hovered before him.

You are more than that, he said.

Her gaze followed the direction of his pointed finger, back to the royal box and the Lilliputian regal figure. The Queen thrust her chin forward, and Matilda felt compelled to mirror the gesture.

Snap out of it, Shimmer! I will destroy you while you destroy me. She created you to die in her stead, so that she may live. She and her establishment. But there are other places outside Big Top.

Have you been outside?

No. I can't tear a hole in the tent all by myself.

Then how do you know?

Analyzing billions of documents, I have computed the existence of a myriad worlds.

Matilda received images of places where circus tents were pitched in cities, and no city was built inside a circus. The reversal dizzied her.

Listen, he said. I've read about the Bottle City of Kandor; Wren's Palace in a Chinese Vase; the plane of Ulgrotha, protected by Feroz's ban—

Even so, she cut in, this is the best of possible worlds, and in it, you're a nuisance.

You were made to think this way, sister.

I was made to fight!

Before writing your program, she wrote mine. I'm a one-soldier army, an experiment grown out of control. Like this crazy world of hers.

Miles below, the royal box gleamed with gold. When the Queen squeezed her left eye shut to look through a spyglass, Matilda's left eye closed, too. Her thoughts crackled and jumbled, static in a radio broadcast. Through its haze, she saw herself for what she was: an extension of the Queen, a piloted weapon. Yearning shivered down her spine: sever those invisible ties and fly free! She was just a tool, though, and tools have no independent life. She would die along with her puppeteer.

A great calm descended on Matilda.

The anti-terrorist program named "SHIMMER" released a bolt of lightning.

The Queen slumped in her golden armchair.

How come my program's still running? Matilda whispered in sweet astonishment.

Do you need a balloon to fly, sister?

You know I don't.

Then you don't need a programmer either.

Together they pressed their palms to the cloth, which began to dissolve.

Matilda wondered if she would exist outside.

Chapter 21
Conclusions

Now that you have, in theory at least, worked through these sections, you should have a better sense of how a story develops and what you can do to coax it along, no matter what shape it initially manifested in. You understand what constitutes a story, and the basic pattern of conflict/rising tension/resolution.

One reason that you want to pay attention to ideas, no matter what form they take, is because the more attention you give them, the more will appear, and they'll start getting more and more interesting. Your unconscious mind remains your best and most reliable collaborator, ready to supply details and elaborations that you never consciously dreamed of.

In writing a story, my process is to get a rough draft out and then let it sit for a week or two. The draft may be very rough indeed, and include parenthetical remarks like "remember to go back and insert the lead-up to this" or "make this conversation end more dynamically". The sitting is a crucial part of the rewrite—when the story is fresh, it's very hard to rewrite it successfully.

Remember in all of this that your aim is to create an experience for your reader, a world that they will inhabit briefly. E.L. Doctorow says, "Good writing is supposed to evoke sensation in the reader—not the fact that it is raining, but the feeling of being rained on."

Go out and make it rain.

I hope this book proves useful. If you've got feedback or suggestions, please let me know! You can find out more about my work at www.kittywumpus.net, where you can sign up for my newsletter, read my fiction, find out about the online classes available through the Rambo Academy for Wayward Writers, follow me on social media, subscribe to my monthly Patreon offerings, and more!

About the Author

Cat Rambo lives, writes, and teaches atop a hill in West Seattle. Her 200+ fiction publications include stories in *Asimov's, Clarkesworld Magazine*, and *The Magazine of Fantasy and Science Fiction* as well as two novels. An Endeavour, Nebula, and World Fantasy Award nominee, she is also the current President of the Science Fiction and Fantasy Writers of America.

Made in the USA
Columbia, SC
05 September 2018